D1174381

CONCEPTS FROM

Tensor Analysis

AND

Differential Geometry

MATHEMATICS IN SCIENCE AND ENGINEERING

A Series of Monographs and Textbooks

Edited by

Richard Bellman

The RAND Corporation, Santa Monica, California

Volume 1. Concepts From Tensor Analysis and Differential Geometry. TRACY Y. THOMAS. 1961

In preparation

Stability By Lyapunov's Direct Method With Applications. JOSEPH LASALLE and SOLOMON LEFSCHETZ

The Optimal Design of Chemical Reactors: A Study in Dynamic Programming. RUTHERFORD ARIS

Plastic Flow and Fracture in Solids. TRACY Y. THOMAS

Differential-Difference Equations. RICHARD BELLMAN and KENNETH L. COOKE

CONCEPTS FROM *Tensor Analysis* AND *Differential Geometry*

TRACY Y. THOMAS

Graduate Institute for Mathematics and Mechanics
Indiana University, Bloomington, Indiana

1961

New York *ACADEMIC PRESS* *London*

ACADEMIC PRESS INC.
111 FIFTH AVENUE
NEW YORK 3, N. Y.

United Kingdom Edition
Published by
ACADEMIC PRESS INC. (LONDON) LTD.
17 OLD QUEEN STREET, LONDON S.W. 1

Library of Congress Catalog Card Number 60-14269

PRINTED IN THE UNITED STATES OF AMERICA

Preface

In the following pages* we have given an introductory account of the subject of tensor analysis and differential geometry. It is hoped that this volume will be suitable for a one-semester course at the graduate level, for students of pure mathematics as well as for those students whose primary interest is in the study of certain aspects of applied mathematics including the theory of relativity, fluid mechanics, elasticity, and plasticity theory.

T. Y. THOMAS

Los Angeles, California
September, 1960

* Prepared under Contract Nonr-908(09), Indiana University, NR 041 037.

Contents

1. Coordinate Manifolds

Consider the set of all ordered sets of n real numbers $(x^1,\ldots,x^n)$ where n is any positive integer. This set will be called the *arithmetic space of n dimensions*. We can refer to the individual sets $(x^1,\ldots,x^n)$ as the points of this space and to the real numbers $x^1,\ldots,x^n$ which enter into the representation of any point $(x^1,\ldots,x^n)$ as the *coordinates* of the point.

Suppose that a set of geometrical points P (undefined objects in the usual mathematical terminology) can be put into (1,1) correspondence with the points of the arithmetic space of n dimensions. This correspondence $P \leftrightarrow (x^1,\ldots,x^n)$ is called a *coordinate system*, more fully a coordinate system covering the set of geometrical points. If $P \leftrightarrow (y^1,\ldots,y^n)$ is another correspondence or coordinate system for the same set of geometrical points P we can write

$$(x^1,\ldots,x^n) \leftrightarrow P \leftrightarrow (y^1,\ldots,y^n).$$

The (1,1) correspondence $(x^1,\ldots,x^n) \leftrightarrow (y^1,\ldots,y^n)$ thus established between the points of the arithmetic space of n dimensions is called a *coordinate transformation*. It can also be expressed by writing

$$y^i = f^i(x^1,\ldots,x^n); \qquad x^i = \phi^i(y^1,\ldots,y^n), \tag{1.1}$$

where $i = 1,\ldots,n$ and the f and ϕ are functions of the coordinates $x^1,\ldots,x^n$ and $y^1,\ldots,y^n$ respectively. Since the correspondence $(x^1,\ldots x^n) \leftrightarrow (y^1,\ldots,y^n)$ is (1,1) it is clear that the first set of equations (1.1) has a unique solution which is given by the second set of these equations and conversely the second set of equations has a unique solution given by the first set of the equations. The correspondence $(x^1,\ldots,x^n) \leftrightarrow (y^1,\ldots,y^n)$ can also be interpreted as a *permutation* or displacement of the arithmetic space of n dimensions into itself. However an interpretation of this character must be abandoned in favor of the strict concept of the coordinate transformation when we deal with point sets which cannot be covered by a single coordinate system.

A function of one or more variables which is continuous and all of whose derivatives exist and are continuous to derivatives of order u inclusive is frequently called a *function of class* C^u. In particular a continuous function is said to be of class C^0 and a function possessing continuous derivatives of all orders is of class C^∞. To include the case of analytic functions we introduce the special symbol $u = A$ and say that an analytic function is of class C^A. If all the functions f in the first set of equations (1.1) are of class C^u it is a well known result in analysis that the functions ϕ appearing in the inverse relationships are likewise of class C^u. When the functions f, and hence the functions ϕ, are of class C^u we say that the coordinate transformation defined by (1.1) is of class C^u.

It can readily be observed that a coordinate transformation of class C^u with $u > 0$, which we interpret to include the analytic case $u = A$, is *regular* in the sense that the functional determinants $|\partial y^i/\partial x^k|$ and $|\partial x^i/\partial y^k|$ are everywhere different from zero. In fact by differentiation of (1.1) we have

$$\frac{\partial y^i}{\partial x^k}\frac{\partial x^k}{\partial y^j} = \delta^i_j, \tag{1.2}$$

where δ^i_j is *Kronecker's delta* with $\delta^i_j = 1$ for $i = j$ and $\delta^i_j = 0$ for i $\neq j$. In writing (1.2) we have employed the summation convention in accordance with which a repeated index in a term is understood to be summed over the permissable values of this index; we shall continue to use the summation convention throughout this book. Taking the determinant of each member of the relation (1.2) we obtain

$$\left|\frac{\partial y^i}{\partial x^k}\right| \cdot \left|\frac{\partial x^k}{\partial y^j}\right| = 1. \tag{1.3}$$

Since neither of the determinants in (1.3) can be infinite at any point P by hypothesis, it follows from (1.3) that these determinants cannot vanish at P, i.e. the transformation (1.1) is regular as above stated.

The entity consisting of the underlying geometrical point set under consideration and the totality of coordinate systems related by transformations (1.1) of class C^u covering this point set, is called a *simple coordinate manifold of class* C^u; the integer n which gives the number of coordinates $x^1,\ldots,x^n$ is called the *dimensionality* of the manifold. Any coordinate system involved in this definition of the simple coordinate manifold of class C^u is said to be *allowable.* Now select any allowable coordinate system S for this manifold (assuming $u \neq 0$) and consider all allowable coordinate systems which are related to S by *proper* coordinate transformations (1.1), i.e. transformations (1.1) whose functional determinants are everywhere positive. The underlying geometrical point set together with these latter coordinate systems is an *oriented* simple coordinate manifold of class C^u. If we select one of the allowable coordinate systems of the original simple manifold, not appearing among the coordinate systems of this oriented simple manifold, it is clear that another oriented simple coordinate manifold of class C^u will be determined by the process described. Thus there are two and in fact, as is easily seen, only two oriented simple coordinate manifolds of class C^u determined by any given simple coordinate manifold of class C^u ($u \neq 0$). One of these may be said to be *positively* oriented and the other *negatively* oriented.

Consider any set of abstract elements $a,b,c,\ldots$ for which there is defined a *law of composition,* usually referred to as multiplication, such that the composition or *product* ab of any ordered pair of elements a and b is an element c of the set. The set of elements in question is then said to form a *group* relative to this law of composition if the following three conditions are satisfied. *First,* $a(bc) = (ab)c$, i.e. *the associative law holds; second, there exists an element* i, *called the unit element, such that* $ai = ia = a$ *for an* *arbitrary element a of the set; and third, to each element a there corresponds an element a^{-1}, called its inverse, such that $aa^{-1} = a^{-1}a = i$.* In particular if the commutative law holds, i.e. $ab = ba$, the group is said to be *Abelian*. Subgroups can be defined in an obvious manner. Various other group concepts might be considered here, e.g. *isomorphic groups, conjugate* and *factor groups, etc.*, but their discussion is not necessary for our purpose.

Now suppose that the elements $a,b,c,\ldots$ are the above coordinate transformations (1.1) of class C^u relating the coordinates of allowable systems of a simple coordinate manifold of class C^u and that the product of any two such elements is the resultant transformation which obviously belongs to the set under consideration. If the unit element i is taken to be the identity transformation and the above element a^{-1} is defined as the transformation inverse to the coordinate transformation a, it is easily seen that the transformations (1.1) constitute a group. We may refer to this group as the *group of the manifold.* Similar remarks of course apply to the coordinate transformations which relate the allowable systems of the two oriented simple coordinate manifolds determined by any simple coordinate manifold of class C^u.

A generalization of the above concept of the simple coordinate manifold is obtained by assuming that any point P of the underlying geometrical point set is contained in a neighborhood N (open set) the points of which can be placed in (1,1) correspondence with the points of an open set of the arithmetic space of n dimensions. The resulting correspondence $P \leftrightarrow (x^1,\ldots,x^n)$ defines a coordinate system for the neighborhood N. Now consider another neighborhood N' and a coordinate system $P \leftrightarrow (y^1,\ldots,y^n)$ for this neighborhood. If the intersection $N \cap N'$ is non-vacuous we can combine the correspondences $P \leftrightarrow (x^1,\ldots,x^n)$ and $P \leftrightarrow (y^1,\ldots,y^n)$ to obtain a coordinate transformation $(x^1,\ldots,x^n) \leftrightarrow (y^1,\ldots,y^n)$ valid in the intersection of the neighborhoods N and N'. The entity consisting of the underlying geometrical point set together with the totality of *allowable* coordinate systems defined over its neighborhoods is now called a *coordinate manifold of n dimensions;* coordinate transformations between the coordinates of allowable coordinate systems are said to be *allowable*. When the allowable coordinate systems are restricted by the requirement that the functions f and ϕ in the equations (1.1), which represent the allowable coordinate transformations, are of class C^u, we say that the manifold is a *coordinate manifold of class* C^u. It is commonly assumed that any (1,1) transformation (1.1) of class C^u of the coordinates $x^1, \ldots x^n$ of an allowable system x is allowable and leads to an allowable coordinate system y for the manifold of class C^u. Transformations (1.1), relating the coordinates of two allowable systems x and y of a coordinate manifold of class C^u $(u \neq 0)$, will be regular; the proof is identical with the above proof of the corresponding result for simple coordinate manifolds of class C^u.

With the exception of the brief discussion of scalars in Sect. 2 the nature of our work requires the differentiability of the functions f or ϕ defining the coordinate transformations (1.1). Hence it will generally be assumed without special mention that the case $u = 0$ is excluded in any reference to a coordinate manifold of class C^u. It will also be assumed implicitly that the class of the manifold is such as to permit the operations of differentiation involved in the problem under consideration and with this understanding the explicit designation of the class C^u of the manifold will usually be omitted.

Remark. An example of a geometrical point set which cannot be covered by a single coordinate system is furnished by a sphere in ordinary Euclidean metric space (defined in Sect. 12). Thus it is obvious that the extension of the simple coordinate manifold to the more general coordinate manifold, e.g. the coordinate manifold of class C^u, is necessary to meet the requirements of differential geometry.

2. Scalars

The quantity called a *scalar* is a point function $f(P)$ defined over a specified set of points P. When the scalar $f(P)$ is defined over the underlying point set of a coordinate manifold of class C^u it is sometimes called a *scalar field* and it can be represented by suitable functions of the coordinates of the various allowable coordinate systems covering the manifold. Thus we have $f(P) = \psi(x^1,\ldots,x^n)$ where ψ is a function of the coordinates $x^1,\ldots,x^n$ of points P in the x system. Similarly $f(P) = \bar{\psi}(\bar{x}^1,\ldots,\bar{x}^n)$ in the $\bar{x}$ system, etc. This gives relations such as

$$\psi(x^1,\ldots,x^n) = \bar{\psi}(\bar{x}^1,\ldots,\bar{x}^n),$$

when $x^1,\ldots,x^n$ and $\bar{x}^1,\ldots,\bar{x}^n$ are the coordinates of the same geometrical point P in the x and $\bar{x}$ systems. The above functions $\psi(x)$ and $\bar{\psi}(x)$ are called the *components of the scalar* in the x and $\bar{x}$ systems respectively.

The scalar f may be said to be of class C^w if the functions giving its components in the various coordinate systems are of class C^w. In the case of an analytic coordinate manifold (coordinate manifold of class C^A) there is obviously no restriction on the class of the scalars which one may consider to be defined over the manifold. However for scalars of class C^w, defined over non-analytic coordinate manifolds of class C^u, we must have $w \neq A$ and $w \leqslant u$ in order that the class of the component functions ψ may be preserved under coordinate transformations.

3. Vectors and Tensors

Let P be an arbitrary point of a coordinate manifold of class C^u and suppose that, corresponding to each of the allowable coordinate systems containing P, there is an ordered set of n numbers associated with this point. Thus if we denote the coordinate systems by x, $\bar{x}$, $\bar{\bar{x}}$, etc., we have

$v^1, v^2, \ldots, v^n$ relative to the x system,

$\bar{v}^1, \bar{v}^2, \ldots, \bar{v}^n$ relative to the $\bar{x}$ system,

$\bar{\bar{v}}^1, \bar{\bar{v}}^2, \ldots, \bar{\bar{v}}^n$ relative to the $\bar{\bar{x}}$ system,

. . . .

. . . .

We then think of an *entity* having $v^1, \ldots, v^n$ as *components* at P relative to the x system; $\bar{v}^1, \ldots, \bar{v}^n$ as components at P relative to the $\bar{x}$ system; etc. This entity is called a *vector* at the point P if its components relative to any two of the above coordinate systems, for example the x and $\bar{x}$ systems, satisfy relations of the form

$$\bar{v}^i = v^k \frac{\partial \bar{x}^i}{\partial x_k}, \qquad (i = 1, \ldots, n). \tag{3.1}$$

More fully this vector is called a *contravariant vector*. A slight modification of the above relations (3.1) leads to the concept of the *covariant vector* at the point P as the entity having components $v_1, v_2, \ldots, v_n$ at P relative to the x system, etc., such that the components transform under coordinate transformations by the equations

$$\bar{v}_i = v_k \frac{\partial x^k}{\partial \bar{x}^i}, \qquad (i = 1, \ldots, n). \tag{3.2}$$

Now consider the equations

$$\bar{\bar{v}}^i = \bar{v}^k \frac{\partial \bar{\bar{x}}^i}{\partial \bar{x}^k}, \qquad (i = 1,\ldots,n), \tag{3.3}$$

expressing the relation between the components of the above contravariant vector in the $\bar{x}$ and $\bar{\bar{x}}$ coordinate systems. Combining (3.1) and (3.3) we have

$$\bar{\bar{v}}^i = \left(v^j \frac{\partial \bar{x}^k}{\partial x^j}\right) \frac{\partial \bar{\bar{x}}^i}{\partial \bar{x}^k} = v^j \left(\frac{\partial \bar{\bar{x}}^i}{\partial \bar{x}^k} \frac{\partial \bar{x}^k}{\partial x^j}\right) = v^j \frac{\partial \bar{\bar{x}}^i}{\partial x^j}.$$

But these are precisely the equations relating the components of the vector in the x and $\bar{\bar{x}}$ systems according to our definition. The fact that no new relations are obtained by the above process of elimination is expressed by saying that the equations (3.1) have the *transitive property*. Similar remarks of course apply to the equations (3.2) for the transformation of the components of a covariant vector.

If v and w are covariant and contravariant vectors respectively at a point P of a coordinate manifold the algebraic combination $v_i w^i$ defines a scalar. This follows from the fact that the quantities $v_i w^i$, $\bar{v}_i \bar{w}^i$, etc., have the same value at P. Thus from (3.1) and (3.2) we obtain

$$\bar{v}_i \bar{w}^i = \left(v_k \frac{\partial x^k}{\partial \bar{x}^i}\right)\left(w^j \frac{\partial \bar{x}^i}{\partial x^j}\right) = v_k w^j \left(\frac{\partial x^k}{\partial \bar{x}^i} \frac{\partial \bar{x}^i}{\partial x^j}\right) = v_k w^j \delta_j^k = v_k w^k.$$

The scalar defined by $v_i w^i$ is called the *scalar product* of the vectors v and w.

A vector defined over a coordinate manifold is called a *vector field*. The class of the vector field is, by definition, the class of the functions giving the vector components in the various allowable coordinate systems of the manifold. Obvious limitations can be placed on the class of the vector field corresponding to the case of the scalar discussed in Sect. 2. Since all quantities including scalars, vectors and tensors, which will enter into our considerations, will habitually be defined over a coordinate manifold or at least within a region (open set) of such a manifold the term *field* will be applicable but will usually, for brevity, be omitted from the discussion.

The definition of the *tensor* appears as a direct extension of the definition of a vector. Thus consider the following sets of quantities

$$
\begin{array}{ll}
T^{i\ldots j}_{k\ldots m} & \text{relative to the } x \text{ system,} \\
\bar{T}^{i\ldots j}_{k\ldots m} & \text{relative to the } \bar{x} \text{ system,} \\
\bar{\bar{T}}^{i\ldots j}_{k\ldots m} & \text{relative to the } \bar{\bar{x}} \text{ system,} \\
\ldots\ldots\ldots\ldots\ldots\ldots & \\
\ldots\ldots\ldots\ldots\ldots\ldots &
\end{array}
$$

defined in the various allowable coordinate systems of a coordinate manifold of class C^u, where each of the indices $i,\ldots,j,k,\ldots,m$ can take on values arbitrarily from the range $1,\ldots,n$. The entity having the above quantities as its components, relative to the coordinate systems indicated, is called a tensor provided the relations between any two sets of these components, e.g. the components $T^{i\ldots j}_{k\ldots m}$ and $\bar{T}^{i\ldots j}_{k\ldots m}$, are of the form

$$
\bar{T}^{i\ldots j}_{k\ldots m} = T^{a\ldots b}_{c\ldots d} \frac{\partial x^c}{\partial \bar{x}^k} \cdots \frac{\partial x^d}{\partial \bar{x}^m} \frac{\partial \bar{x}^i}{\partial x^a} \cdots \frac{\partial \bar{x}^j}{\partial x^b} \tag{3.4}
$$

in the intersection of the neighborhoods covered by the x and $\bar{x}$ coordinates systems. The demonstration of the transitive property of the equations (3.1) and (3.2) can be extended immediately to the equations (3.4).

The tensor defined above is sometimes referred to as a *mixed tensor* to indicate the fact that both superscripts $i,\ldots,j$ and subscripts $k,\ldots,m$ appear in the symbol of its components. In particular a tensor having components $T^{i\ldots j}$ is called a *contravariant tensor* and one with components $T_{k\ldots m}$ is called a *covariant tensor*. The number of indices in the symbol for the components of a tensor is called the *rank* of the tensor.

The following is a list of some of the simple algebraic operations that can be performed on tensors; all of these operations can be proved directly by recourse to the law of transformation (3.4) of the components of the tensor.

(a) Addition

If the components $A^{i\ldots j}_{k\ldots m}$ and $B^{i\ldots j}_{k\ldots m}$ of two tensors A and B contain the same number of covariant and contravariant indices the corresponding components of these tensors can be added to produce the components of a single tensor. Thus

$$C^{i\ldots j}_{k\ldots m} = A^{i\ldots j}_{k\ldots m} + B^{i\ldots j}_{k\ldots m}$$

are the components of a tensor C called the *sum* of the tensors A and B. Similarly the difference between the corresponding components of the tensors A and B constitutes the components of a single tensor.

(b) Multiplication

If we multiply all the components $A^{i\ldots j}_{k\ldots m}$ of a tensor A by all the components $B^{p\ldots q}_{r\ldots s}$ of a tensor B, not necessarily of the same rank as the tensor A, we obtain a set of quantities

$$C^{i\ldots j\,p\ldots q}_{k\ldots m\,r\ldots s} = A^{i\ldots j}_{k\ldots m}\,B^{p\ldots q}_{r\ldots s}$$

which constitute the components of a new tensor. In particular a new tensor is obtained by multiplying the components of a given tensor by a scalar.

(c) CONTRACTION

The components $A^{ij\ldots k}_{pq\ldots r}$ of a tensor can be used to define a set of quantities

$$B^{j\ldots k}_{q\ldots r} = A^{ij\ldots k}_{iq\ldots r}$$

which possess tensor character. The components $B^{j\ldots k}_{q\ldots r}$ are said to be obtained from the components $A^{ij\ldots k}_{pq\ldots r}$ by contracting the indices i and p. Any index of the set $ij\ldots k$ and any index of the set $pq\ldots r$ can be contracted in this manner to form the components of a new tensor.

A tensor is said to be *symmetric* with respect to two contravariant indices (superscripts) or with respect to two covariant indices (subscripts) which appear in the symbol of its components if the interchange of these indices leaves unaltered the values of all components of the tensor. It is *skew-symmetric* if the interchange of the indices changes the algebraic sign of all components of the tensor. One can readily verify that the symmetric or skew-symmetric properties of the components of a tensor persist under transformations of coordinates. A tensor which is symmetric or skew-symmetric with respect to all adjacent pairs of contravariant and covariant indices in the symbol of its components is spoken of simply as a symmetric or skew-symmetric tensor.

Remark 1. It is an interesting observation that the quantities δ^i_j defined above are the components of a mixed tensor. This follows in fact from the identical relations

$$\delta^i_j = \frac{\partial \bar{x}^i}{\partial x^k}\frac{\partial x^k}{\partial \bar{x}^j} = \delta^m_k \frac{\partial \bar{x}^i}{\partial x^m}\frac{\partial x^k}{\partial \bar{x}^j}\,.$$

Remark 2. By a simple modification of the transformation equations (3.4) one arrives at the definition of a *relative tensor* or *tensor of weight* W where W is an arbitrary constant. The modified equations (3.4) giving the transformation of the components of a relative tensor of weight W are

$$\bar{T}^{i\ldots j}_{k\ldots m} = |\partial x/\partial \bar{x}|^W T^{a\ldots b}_{c\ldots d} \frac{\partial x^c}{\partial \bar{x}^k} \cdots \frac{\partial x^d}{\partial \bar{x}^m} \frac{\partial \bar{x}^i}{\partial x^a} \cdots \frac{\partial \bar{x}^j}{\partial x^b}, \tag{3.5}$$

where the quantity $|\partial x/\partial \bar{x}|$ is the functional determinant or jacobian of the transformation relating the coordinates of the x and $\bar{x}$ systems. It is readily shown that the relations (3.5) enjoy the transitive property which is a basic requirement in the concept of a tensor. The terms mixed, contravariant, covariant, etc., carry over to tensors of arbitrary weight W as do also the above properties of addition, multiplication and contraction. Thus two tensors of the same kind, i.e. which have the same number of covariant and contravariant indices and the same weights, can be added to give a tensor of this kind. However when the product of two tensors of weights W and W' is formed the result is a tensor of weight $W + W'$. When one speaks of a tensor without explicit mention of its weight it is customary to understand a tensor of weight zero or *absolute tensor*, as it is sometimes called, unless it is clear that the tensor in question has weight $W \neq 0$ and the omission of the weight is merely for the purpose of brevity.

4. A Special Skew-symmetric Tensor

We shall now consider a skew-symmetric tensor e which has certain interesting formal properties. Since the case $n = 3$ is of particular importance from the standpoint of the applications we specifically treat this case for which the components of the tensor e may be denoted by e_{ijk} and defined as follows:

(a) $e_{ijk} = 0$ *if two indices* i,j,k *are the same*;

(b) $e_{ijk} = 1$ *if* i,j,k *is an even permutation of* 1,2,3;

(c) $e_{ijk} = -1$ *if* i,j,k *is an odd permutation of* 1,2,3.

It will be shown that the above quantities e_{ijk} are of tensor character under transformations of the allowable coordinate systems of a three dimensional coordinate manifold of class C^u.

As a first step in the proof of this result let us consider the expansion of a third order determinant, namely

$$|a^i_j| = \begin{vmatrix} a^1_1 & a^1_2 & a^1_3 \\ a^2_1 & a^2_2 & a^2_3 \\ a^3_1 & a^3_2 & a^3_3 \end{vmatrix} = \Sigma \pm a^i_1 a^j_2 a^k_3,$$

where the summation Σ involves all terms which can be obtained from the one written down explicitly by replacing i,j,k by permutations (without repetitions) of the numbers 1,2,3; also the $+$ sign is to be inserted before any term of this sum for which i,j,k is an even permutation of 1,2,3 while the $-$ sign is to be used if i,j,k is an odd permutation. All this is now taken care of very conveniently by means of the quantities e_{ijk} defined above and use of the summation convention. In fact we see immediately that we can write

$$|a^i_j| = e_{ijk}\, a^i_1\, a^j_2\, a^k_3. \tag{4.1}$$

It is readily seen that the above equations (4.1) can be extended to give

$$|a^i_j|\, e_{pqr} = e_{ijk}\, a^i_p\, a^j_q\, a^k_r, \tag{4.2}$$

where the p,q,r are *free indices*, i.e. these indices can be assigned values 1,2,3 at will. Thus both members of (4.2) reduce to zero if two of the indices p,q,r have the same value; this is a direct consequence of the skew-symmetry of the e_{ijk}. On the other hand according as p,q,r is an even or an odd permutation of 1,2,3 the two members of (4.2) become $|a^i_j|$ or $-|a^i_j|$ respectively. Replacing the elements a^i_j in (4.2) by the corresponding coordinate derivatives $\partial x^i/\partial \bar{x}^j$ we now have

$$e_{pqr} = |\partial x/\partial \bar{x}|^{-1}\, e_{ijk} \frac{\partial x^i}{\partial \bar{x}^p} \frac{\partial x^j}{\partial \bar{x}^q} \frac{\partial x^k}{\partial x^r}. \tag{4.3}$$

But this means that the skew-symmetric quantities e_{ijk} are the components of a relative covariant tensor e of weight -1 in the three dimensional coordinate manifold under consideration.

It is an interesting observation that the quantities e_{ijk} can also be regarded as the components of a contravariant tensor of weight $+1$ in the three dimensional coordinate manifold. Denoting the e_{ijk} by the symbols e^{ijk} in connection with this result we first show that

$$|a^i_j|\, e^{pqr} = e^{ijk}\, a^p_i\, a^q_j\, a^r_k, \tag{4.4}$$

corresponding to (4.2). Hence, identifying the a^i_j with the derivatives $\partial \bar{x}^i/\partial x^j$, we obtain

$$e^{pqr} = |\partial x/\partial \bar{x}|\, e^{ijk} \frac{\partial \bar{x}^p}{\partial x^i} \frac{\partial \bar{x}^q}{\partial x^j} \frac{\partial \bar{x}^r}{\partial x^k}, \tag{4.5}$$

by which the result is established.

Remark 1. By an obvious extension of the above definition of the quantities e_{ijk} we can define skew-symmetric quantities $e_{ij\ldots k}$ or $e^{ij\ldots k}$, involving n indices, which can be used to obtain equations similar to (4.2) and (4.4) for the expansion of a determinant of the n-th order. From these equations it will follow, by the above procedure, that the $e_{ij\ldots k}$ or $e^{ij\ldots k}$ constitute the components of a skew-symmetric covariant or contravariant tensor of weight -1 or $+1$ respectively in an n dimensional coordinate manifold.

In particular the quantities $e_{\alpha\beta}$ and $e^{\alpha\beta}$ defined by

$$\left.\begin{array}{llll} e_{11}=0; & e_{12}=1; & e_{21}=-1; & e_{22}=0, \\ e^{11}=0; & e^{12}=1; & e^{21}=-1; & e^{22}=0, \end{array}\right\}$$

are the components of a skew-symmetric covariant tensor of weight -1 and a skew-symmetric contravariant tensor of weight $+1$ in a two dimensional coordinate manifold. Between the components $e_{\alpha\beta}$ and $e^{\alpha\beta}$ we have the relations

$$e_{\alpha\beta}e^{\alpha\gamma}=\delta^{\gamma}_{\beta}. \tag{4.6}$$

Correspondingly we readily observe that the skew-symmetric components e_{ijk} and e^{ijk}, which are defined in a three dimensional coordinate manifold, are such that

$$e_{ijk}\,e^{ipq}=\delta^{p}_{j}\,\delta^{q}_{k}-\delta^{p}_{k}\,\delta^{q}_{j}. \tag{4.7}$$

Remark 2. Equations of the type (4.2) and (4.4) can be used to deduce several of the well known properties of determinants. By assigning equal values to two of the indices p,q,r in (4.2) we obtain the result that a determinant vanishes if two of its columns are identical; also by interchanging two of these indices it follows that the interchange of two columns of a determinant changes its algebraic sign. Similarly it follows from (4.4) that a determinant vanishes if two of its rows are identical and that the interchange of two rows produces a change of algebraic sign in the value of the determinant.

These equations likewise permit an easy derivation of the well known theorem on the multiplication of two determinants of the n-th order. Thus, using the representative relations (4.2) and (4.4), we have

$$|a^{i}_{j}|\,|b^{k}_{m}|=(|a^{i}_{j}|e_{pqr})b^{p}_{1}\,b^{q}_{2}\,b^{r}_{3}=e_{ijk}\,a^{i}_{p}\,a^{j}_{q}\,a^{k}_{r}\,b^{p}_{1}\,b^{q}_{2}\,b^{r}_{3}.$$

But, substituting c^{i}_{m} for the combination $a^{i}_{p}\,b^{p}_{m}$ in the right member of this relation, we can write

$$|a^{i}_{j}|\,|b^{k}_{m}|=e_{ijk}\,c^{i}_{1}\,c^{j}_{2}\,c^{k}_{3}=|c^{i}_{j}|.$$

Expressed in words this shows that the product of the determinants $|a^{i}_{j}|$ and $|b^{i}_{j}|$ is the determinant $|c^{i}_{j}|$ in which the element in the ith row and jth column is the sum of the products of the corresponding elements in the ith row of $|a^{i}_{j}|$ and the jth column of $|b^{i}_{j}|$.

5. The Vector Product. Curl of a Vector

The tensor e defined in Sect. 4 can be used in the definition of the well known *vector product* of two vectors A and B in a coordinate manifold of three dimensions. According as the vectors A and B are covariant or contravariant vectors we define their vector product to be the vector C having components represented by one or the other of the following two sets of equations

$$C^i = e^{ijk} A_j B_k; \qquad C_i = e_{ijk} A^j B^k. \tag{5.1}$$

As defined by the equations (5.1) the vector product of two absolute covariant vectors A and B is a relative contravariant vector C of weight $+1$ while the vector product of two absolute contravariant vectors A and B is a relative covariant vector C of weight -1 in the three dimensional coordinate manifold.

An analogous application of the tensor e furnishes the definition of the *curl of a vector* V in a coordinate manifold of three dimensions. Thus if V is an absolute covariant vector whose components $V_i(x)$ are differentiable functions of the coordinates x^1, x^2, x^3 of the allowable coordinate systems covering the manifold we see immediately from the equations of transformation of the components of V that the quantities

$$\frac{\partial V_i}{\partial x^k} - \frac{\partial V_k}{\partial x^j}$$

are the components of a covariant tensor of the second rank. Hence the quantities W^i defined by

$$W^i = \frac{1}{2} e^{ijk} \left(\frac{\partial V_j}{\partial x^k} - \frac{\partial V_k}{\partial x^j} \right) = e^{ijk} \frac{\partial V_j}{\partial x^k} \tag{5.2}$$

are the components of a relative vector W of weight $+1$ in the three dimensional manifold. The vector W defined by (5.2) is called the curl or *rotation* of the vector V.

6. Riemann Spaces

The concept of distance does not enter into the preceding discussion. We now introduce this concept by the assumption that the distance ds between two infinitely nearby points P and Q in a coordinate manifold of n dimensions is given by

$$ds^2 = g_{ij}\, dx^i\, dx^j, \tag{6.1}$$

where the right member of this equation is a positive definite quadratic form in the coordinate differences dx^i of the points P and Q; the coefficients g_{ij} can be taken to be symmetric in the indices i and j without loss of generality. A coordinate manifold of n dimensions over which such a quadratic differential form is defined is called an *n dimensional Riemann space.*

The use of (6.1) to determine distance involves the condition that the quadratic form in the right member of this equation is invariant under allowable coordinate transformations. But from this invariance one can immediately infer that the coefficients g_{ij} are the components of a symmetric covariant tensor, i.e.

$$\bar{g}_{ij}(\bar{x}) = g_{ab}(x)\,\frac{\partial x^a}{\partial \bar{x}^i}\,\frac{\partial x^b}{\partial \bar{x}^j}\,, \tag{6.2}$$

as the result of an allowable coordinate transformation $x \leftrightarrow \bar{x}$ in the manifold. The tensor having the quantities g_{ij} as its components is called the *fundamental metric tensor* of the Riemann space. We shall say that the Riemann space is of class C^w if the components g_{ij} are of class C^w in the allowable coordinate systems covering the manifold. In the case of a Riemann space of class C^w $(w \neq A)$ it will be assumed that coordinate transformations $x \leftrightarrow \bar{x}$ of class C^{w+1} are allowable since such transformations will preserve the class of the functions g_{ij} without being unnecessarily restricted; for an analytic Riemann space, i.e. a Riemann space of class C^A, it is required that the allowable coordinate transformations $x \leftrightarrow \bar{x}$ be of class C^A.

Since the quadratic differential form (6.1) is positive definite by hypothesis it follows that the determinant g of its coefficients is positive, i.e. explicitly

$$g = \begin{vmatrix} g_{11} & g_{12} & \cdots & g_{1n} \\ g_{21} & g_{22} & \cdots & g_{2n} \\ \cdots & \cdots & \cdots & \cdots \\ \cdots & \cdots & \cdots & \cdots \\ g_{n1} & g_{n2} & \cdots & g_{nn} \end{vmatrix} > 0. \tag{6.3}$$

By equating the determinants of the two members of the equations (6.2) and then extracting the square roots of both sides of the resulting equation we obtain

$$\sqrt{\bar{g}} = |\partial x / \partial \bar{x}| \sqrt{g}, \tag{6.4}$$

provided the determinant $|\partial x / \partial \bar{x}|$ is positive. Now if the covering of the Riemann space by its allowable coordinate systems is such that the functional determinant or jacobian $|\partial x / \partial \bar{x}|$ of every coordinate transformation is always positive the Riemann space will be said to be *oriented* (Sect. 1). *Hence the quantity* $\sqrt{g}$ *appears as a relative scalar of weight* 1 *in the case of an oriented Riemann space.*

Use of the relation (6.4) permits us to replace the relative tensor e defined in Sect. 4 by an absolute tensor ε. For the special case of three dimensions this tensor ε will have components ε_{ijk} or ε^{ijk} defined as follows

$$\varepsilon_{ijk} = \sqrt{g}\, e_{ijk}; \qquad \varepsilon^{ijk} = \frac{e^{ijk}}{\sqrt{g}}.$$

Replacing the e's by the corresponding ε's in the equations (5.1) and (5.2) we now have

$$C^i = \varepsilon^{ijk} A_j B_k; \qquad C_i = \varepsilon_{ijk} A^j B^k, \tag{6.5}$$

$$W^i = \tfrac{1}{2} \varepsilon^{ijk} \left(\frac{\partial V_j}{\partial x^k} - \frac{\partial V_k}{\partial x^j} \right) = \varepsilon^{ijk} \frac{\partial V_j}{\partial x^k}. \tag{6.6}$$

Hence in an oriented Riemann space of three dimensions we can define the vector product of two absolute vectors A and B as the absolute vector C whose components are given by the first or second of the relations (6.5) according as the vectors A and B are covariant or contravariant respectively; also the curl or rotation of an absolute vector V can be defined as the absolute vector W with components W^i given by (6.6).

The fundamental metric tensor having the symmetric covariant components g_{ij} can be represented by a symmetric contravariant tensor whose components g^{ij} are defined by the equations

$$g^{ij} = \frac{\text{cofactor of } g_{ij} \text{ in the det. } |g_{ij}|}{|g_{ij}|}. \tag{6.7}$$

To show that the symmetric quantities g^{ij} given by (6.7) in the allowable coordinate systems in the Riemann space are the components of a contravariant tensor let us first observe that

$$g^{ij} g_{im} = \delta^i_m. \tag{6.8}$$

For definiteness in our demonstration let us suppose that the g_{ij} are the components of the metric tensor in an x coordinate system and let us consider the equations corresponding to (6.8), namely

$$\bar{g}^{ij} \bar{g}_{im} = \delta^j_m, \tag{6.9}$$

which involve the metric tensor components $\bar{g}_{ij}$ and the quantities $\bar{g}^{ij}$ in an $\bar{x}$ system. From (6.2) and (6.9) we immediately obtain

$$\bar{g}^{ij} g_{ab} \frac{\partial x^a}{\partial \bar{x}^i} \frac{\partial x^b}{\partial \bar{x}^m} = \delta^j_m. \tag{6.10}$$

Now multiply both members of (6.10) by the quantity

$$g^{cd} \frac{\partial \bar{x}^m}{\partial x^c} \frac{\partial \bar{x}^k}{\partial x^d},$$

and sum on all repeated indices in the usual manner. But this leads to the relations

$$\bar{g}^{jk} = g^{cd} \frac{\partial \bar{x}^j}{\partial x^c} \frac{\partial \bar{x}^k}{\partial x^d}, \tag{6.11}$$

and hence proves the contravariant character of the quantities g^{ij} defined by (6.7).

By means of the covariant components g_{ij} and the contravariant components g^{ij} of the fundamental metric tensor we can modify the covariant or contravariant nature of a tensor by raising or lowering the indices in the symbol of its components. Thus the components T^i_{jk} of a tensor T can be lowered or raised as follows:

$$T_{mjk} = g_{im} T^i_{jk}; \qquad T^{im}_j = g^{mk} T^i_{jk}; \quad \text{etc.}$$

Conversely we can pass from the above components T_{mjk} and T^{im}_j to the original components T^i_{jk} by this process of raising or lowering the indices in question. These various sets of components therefore appear as the components of *essentially* the same tensor T.

Remark 1. By means of the process of raising or lowering indices the scalar product of a covariant and a contravariant vector, defined in Sect. 3, can be extended to the case where both of the product vectors are covariant or contravariant in character. Thus the scalar product of the vectors A and B is the scalar $g_{ij} A^i B^i$ or the scalar $g^{ij} A_i B_j$ according as A and B are contravariant or covariant vectors.

Remark 2. In accordance with the relations (6.8) the δ^i_j can be interpreted as the result of raising one of the indices of the components g_{ij}. Hence the Kronecker δ appears as a mixed form, i.e. a tensor whose symbol involves both covariant and contravariant indices, of the fundamental metric tensor.

Remark 3. It is a well known algebraic result that a positive definite quadratic form can be reduced to the sum of the squares of its variables by a linear transformation. Hence at any point P of a Riemann space the differential form (6.1) can be reduced to the sum of the squares of the quantities dx^i as the result of an allowable transformation of the coordinates of the manifold. In other words it is always possible to choose a coordinate system relative to which the quantities $g_{ij} = \delta_{ij}$ at an arbitrary point P. Moreover this can be accomplished by a proper coordinate transformation, i.e. a transformation whose functional determinant is positive. In fact if the transformation $x \leftrightarrow \bar{x}$ changing the values of the g_{ij} to the values δ_{ij} at P is not proper then the g_{ij} can be reduced to the values δ_{ij} at P by the proper transformation $x \leftrightarrow y$ which is the resultant of the transformation $x \leftrightarrow \bar{x}$ and the transformation $\bar{x} \leftrightarrow y$ such that $\bar{x}^1 = -y^1$, $\bar{x}^k = y^k$ for $k = 2, \ldots, n$. *Hence it is always possible to select an allowable coordinate system relative to which the components g_{ij} of the fundamental metric tensor have the values δ_{ij} at an arbitrary point P of an oriented Riemann space.*

Remark 4. Corresponding to the above quantities ε_{ijk} and ε^{ijk} we can define quantities

$$\varepsilon_{\alpha\beta} = \sqrt{g}\, e_{\alpha\beta}; \qquad e^{\alpha\beta} = \frac{\varepsilon^{\alpha\beta}}{\sqrt{g}},$$

in the case of an oriented Riemann space of two dimensions; as so defined the $\varepsilon_{\alpha\beta}$ and the $\varepsilon^{\alpha\beta}$ are the components of an absolute skew-symmetric covariant tensor and an absolute skew-symmetric contravariant tensor respectively. It is now readily seen that the relations (4.6) and (4.7) can be modified to read

$$\varepsilon_{\sigma\alpha}\, \varepsilon^{\sigma\beta} = \delta^\beta_\alpha; \qquad \varepsilon_{ijk}\, \varepsilon^{ipq} = \delta^p_j\, \delta^q_k - \delta^p_k\, \delta^q_j. \tag{6.12}$$

In fact, choosing a coordinate system relative to which the components of the fundamental metric tensors are equal to the corresponding Kronecker deltas at a point P of the two and three dimensional oriented spaces, the two sets of relations (6.12) become (4.6) and (4.7) respectively at the point P; hence the validity of (6.12) in general follows from the fact that the members of these relations are individually the components of absolute tensors as implied by their indices.

Other relations between the components of these tensors ε are

$$\varepsilon^{\alpha\beta} = g^{\alpha\sigma} g^{\beta\tau} \varepsilon_{\sigma\tau}; \qquad \varepsilon_{\alpha\beta} = g_{\alpha\sigma} g_{\beta\tau} \varepsilon^{\sigma\tau}, \tag{6.13}$$

$$\varepsilon^{ijk} = g^{ia} g^{jb} g^{kc} \varepsilon_{abc}; \qquad \varepsilon_{ijk} = g_{ia} g_{jb} g_{kc} \varepsilon^{abc}. \tag{6.14}$$

Both (6.13) and (6.14) can be proved by the argument used to establish the relations (6.12). Similarly we can show the validity of the relations

$$g_{\sigma\tau}\, \varepsilon^{\sigma\alpha}\, \varepsilon^{\tau\beta} = g^{\alpha\beta}; \qquad g^{\sigma\tau}\, \varepsilon_{\sigma\alpha}\, \varepsilon_{\tau\beta} = g_{\alpha\beta}, \tag{6.15}$$

$$\left.\begin{aligned} g_{ab}\, \varepsilon^{ajk}\, \varepsilon^{bqr} &= g^{jq}\, g^{kr} - g^{jr}\, g^{kq}, \\ g^{ab}\, \varepsilon_{ajk}\, \varepsilon_{bqr} &= g_{jq}\, g_{kr} - g_{jr}\, g_{kq}, \end{aligned}\right\} \tag{6.16}$$

which will have application in the following work. In this connection it should be noted that the strict invariance of (6.15) and (6.16) under coordinate transformations does not require that the Riemann space be oriented due to the manner in which the ε's are involved in these relations.

In the remainder of this section we shall comment briefly on the measurement of lengths, angles, volume, etc. which are possible in a Riemann space because of the metric structure.

(a) Length of a vector

By definition the square of the length of a contravariant vector ξ is given by $g_{ij}\, \xi^i\, \xi^j$. Similarly the square of the length of a covariant vector ξ is $g^{ij}\, \xi_i\, \xi_j$. As so defined the length of a vector is a scalar which is obviously independent of the covariant or contravariant representation of the vector.

(b) Length of a curve

By a *regular* curve C in a Riemann space we shall understand a locus which is determined by equations of the form $x^i = \phi^i(t)$ in the various allowable coordinate systems where the functions $\phi^i(t)$ are differentiable and such that

$$g_{ij}\, \frac{d\phi^j}{dt}\, \frac{d\phi^j}{dt} > 0. \tag{6.17}$$

Since the form (6.1) is positive definite the inequality (6.17) is equivalent to the condition that not all of the derivatives of the functions $\phi^i(t)$ will vanish for any value of the parameter t. The length s of a regular curve C in a Riemann space from the point A, corresponding to the value $t = t_0$ of the parameter, to the variable point P, determined by an arbitrary value of the parameter t, is by definition

$$s = \int_{t_0}^{t} \sqrt{g_{ij} \frac{dx^i}{dt} \frac{dx^j}{dt}}\, dt. \tag{6.18}$$

Since the integrand in this equation is a scalar the length s will be independent of coordinate transformations in the Riemann space. Moreover the equation (6.18) can be regarded as defining a (1,1) parameter transformation $t \leftrightarrow s$ since the derivative ds/dt cannot vanish on account of (6.17); hence the parameter s, which can thus be introduced, will represent the distance, measured along the curve C, of the variable point P from the above fixed point A. As defined by (6.18) the length of the curve C is easily seen to be independent of the parameterization.

(c) Angle determined by two directions. Orthogonality

Let ξ^i be the components of a non-vanishing contravariant vector ξ, i.e. not all the quantities ξ^i are equal to zero, at a point P of a coordinate manifold of n dimensions. We then say that the set of vectors having the components $k\xi^i$, where k is an arbitrary *positive* constant determines a *direction* at P; for brevity we refer to this as the direction ξ. The direction associated with the set of vectors with components $-k\xi^i$ is said to be *opposite* to the direction ξ.

The angle θ determined by the directions ξ and ζ in a Riemann space is defined by the equation

$$\cos\theta = \frac{g_{ij}\, \xi^i\, \zeta^j}{\sqrt{g_{ab}\, \xi^a\, \xi^b}\, \sqrt{g_{ab}\, \zeta^a\, \zeta^b}}\,. \tag{6.19}$$

This formula has the required property that the angle θ remains unchanged if the vector ξ is replaced by any of the vectors $k\xi$ which are associated with the same direction as the vector ξ and a similar remark of course applies to the vector ζ. Moreover if $\xi^i = -\zeta^i$ so that ξ and ζ determine opposite directions the right member of (6.19) reduces to -1 and hence θ is $\pm 180°$. The vectors or directions ξ and ζ are said to be *orthogonal* or *perpendicular* if the right member of (6.19) is equal to zero.

In particular if ξ and ζ are *unit vectors,* i.e. if the lengths of the vectors are equal to 1, the above formula becomes

$$\cos\theta = g_{ij}\,\xi^j\,\zeta^j. \tag{6.20}$$

Remark 5. To show that it is legitimate to employ the formula (6.19) for the determination of the angle θ we must prove that this formula is consistent with the requirement $|\cos\theta| \leqslant 1$ where the bars denotes absolute value. Let us first suppose that the two vectors are proportional, i.e. that we can put $\xi^i = a\zeta^i$ where a is a positive or negative constant. Then (6.19) gives $\cos\theta = 1$ for a positive and $\cos\theta = -1$ for a negative; in the first case the angle determined by the directions ξ and ζ is zero and in the second case it is equal to two right angles. Now assume that ξ and ζ are not proportional so that we cannot find constants μ and ν, not both zero, such that $\mu\xi^i + \nu\zeta^i$ vanishes. Then make the substitution $\eta^i = \mu\xi^i + \nu\zeta^i$ in the quadratic form $g_{ij}\,\eta^i\,\eta^j$ which therefore becomes

$$g_{ij}\,\eta^i\,\eta^j = \mu^2\psi(\xi,\xi) + 2\mu\nu\psi(\xi,\zeta) + \nu^2\psi(\zeta,\zeta),$$

where

$$\left.\begin{aligned} \psi(\xi,\xi) &= g_{ij}\,\xi^i\,\xi^j, \\ \psi(\xi,\zeta) &= g_{ij}\,\xi^i\,\zeta^j, \\ \psi(\zeta,\zeta) &= g_{ij}\,\zeta^i\,\zeta^j. \end{aligned}\right\}$$

Since the η^i cannot all vanish for μ, ν not both equal to zero, it follows that

$$\mu^2\psi(\xi,\xi) + 2\mu\nu\psi(\xi,\zeta) + \nu^2\psi(\zeta,\zeta) > 0, \tag{6.21}$$

provided the real constants μ, ν do not both vanish; hence

$$\psi(\xi,\xi)\psi(\zeta,\zeta) - \psi^2(\xi,\zeta) > 0,$$

since otherwise it would be possible to find real constants μ, ν not both zero such that the left member of (6.21) would be equal to zero. Substitution of the above quadratic forms for the ψ in this last inequality shows immediately that the absolute value of the right member of (6.19) is less than unity.

(d) Volume of a region

The volume of a region R in a Riemann space is defined by the integral

$$\int\int\cdots\int\sqrt{g}\,dx^1 dx^2\ldots dx_n, \tag{6.22}$$

where the integration is extended over the region R. As so defined the volume of R is independent of coordinate transformations, i.e. of the coordinate systems used to cover the region R. We shall not give a formal demonstration of this fact but will content ourselves with the observation that in the special case of a Euclidean metric space of three dimensions (defined in Sect. 12) referred to a system of rectangular cartesian coordinates, with which one is primarily concerned in the physical applications, the relative scalar $\sqrt{g} = 1$, and hence the above integral (6.22) reduces to the triple integral by which the volume of a region is expressed in books on elementary calculus.

(e) Geodesic curves

Consider a regular curve C joining two points A and B of a Riemann space of n dimensions. Let the curve C have as its equations

$$x^i = \phi^i(s), \qquad a \leqslant s \leqslant b,$$

where s denotes the arc length measured from the fixed point A. Also consider a one parameter family of nearby curves which likewise join the points A and B and which have equations

$$x^i = \psi^i(s,\varepsilon), \qquad a \leqslant s \leqslant b, \tag{6.23}$$

where the ψ^i are continuous and differentiable functions of the two parameters s and ε for values of s satisfying the above inequality and values of ε in the neighborhood of $\varepsilon = 0$. We assume that $\psi^i(s, 0) = \phi^i(s)$, i.e. the curve of the family corresponding to $\varepsilon = 0$ is the curve C. Also it follows that $\psi^i(a, \varepsilon)$ and $\psi^i(b, \varepsilon)$ are independent of the parameter ε since all curves of the family pass through the points A and B by hypothesis.

The length of any curve of the family is given by

$$l(\varepsilon) = \int_a^b \sqrt{g_{ij} \frac{\partial x^i}{\partial s} \frac{\partial x^j}{\partial s}}\, ds. \tag{6.24}$$

If the first variation $\delta l = 0$, the above curve C will be said to have a stationary length within the family of curves under consideration. A curve C will be called a *geodesic* if it has a stationary length within *every* family of curves (6.23). It can be shown that a geodesic curve C satisfies the system of differential equations

$$\frac{d^2 x^i}{ds^2} + \Gamma^i_{jk} \frac{dx^j}{ds} \frac{dx^k}{ds} = 0, \tag{6.25}$$

where the functions Γ are defined by

$$\Gamma^i_{jk} = \tfrac{1}{2} g^{im} \left(\frac{\partial g_{mj}}{\partial x^k} + \frac{\partial g_{mk}}{\partial x^i} - \frac{\partial g_{jk}}{\partial x^m} \right); \tag{6.26}$$

these functions are called *Christoffel symbols* and they will have an important application in the following work.

Remark 6. To deduce the equations (6.25) let us first denote the expression under the radical in (6.24) by U for simplicity; then $U = 1$ for $\varepsilon = 0$ since the parameter s represents arc length along the curve C. To a first approximation the curve determined by a value of ε ($\neq 0$) can be considered to be obtained by making a displacement of C such that the point of C, corresponding to the value s of the arc length, undergoes a displacement

$$\delta x^i = \varepsilon \xi^i(s); \qquad \xi^i = \left(\frac{\partial x^i}{\partial \varepsilon} \right)_{\varepsilon = 0}.$$

The displacement δx^i vanishes at the end points A and B of the curve C. For the first variation of the length l defined by (6.24) we have

$$\delta l = \varepsilon \left(\frac{dl}{d\varepsilon} \right)_{\varepsilon = 0} = \int_a^b \frac{\delta U}{2\sqrt{U}} \, ds,$$

or

$$\delta l = \tfrac{1}{2} \int_a^b \delta U \, ds, \tag{6.27}$$

since $U = 1$ for the curve C. Now

$$\frac{\partial U}{\partial \varepsilon} = \frac{\partial g_{ij}}{\partial x^k} \frac{\partial x^i}{\partial s} \frac{\partial x^j}{\partial s} \frac{\partial x^k}{\partial \varepsilon} + 2 \, g_{ij} \frac{\partial x^i}{\partial s} \frac{\partial^2 x^j}{\partial \varepsilon \partial s}.$$

Hence

$$\delta U = \varepsilon \frac{\partial g_{ij}}{\partial x^k} v^i v^j \xi^k + 2 \, \varepsilon \, g_{ij} \, v^i \frac{d\xi^j}{ds}, \tag{6.28}$$

where we have put

$$v^i = \left(\frac{\partial x^i}{\partial s} \right)_{\varepsilon = 0}.$$

Substituting (6.28) into (6.27) and integrating by parts, we obtain

$$\delta l = \varepsilon \int_a^b \left[\frac{1}{2} \frac{\partial g_{ij}}{\partial x^k} v^i v^j - \frac{d}{ds} (g_{ik} \, v^i) \right] \xi^i(s) \, ds, \tag{6.29}$$

when use is made of the fact that $\xi^i(s)$ vanishes at the end points A and B. Now the quantities $\xi^i(s)$ can evidently have arbitrary values for any value of the parameter s due to the generality permitted in the selection of the family of curves given by (6.23). Hence, putting $\delta l = 0$, it follows that the bracket expression in the above relation (6.29) must vanish along C; this leads immediately to the equations (6.25).

Among the totality of geodesic curves joining the points A and B in a Riemann space there will evidently be one possessing the least length of any geodesic joining these points; in particular, if there is only one geodesic joining the points A and B, this will be the curve of shortest length. For example, if our space is of the nature of the surface of a cylinder, curves such as C and C' in Fig. 1 may be geodesics; in fact for this case there will be an infinity of geodesics determined by encircling the cylinder 0,1,2,... times, the geodesic C being the curve of actual shortest length between the points A and B. There is an interesting property connected with any geodesic which can be stated roughly by saying that it represents the shortest curve between any two of its points provided these points are sufficiently close together.

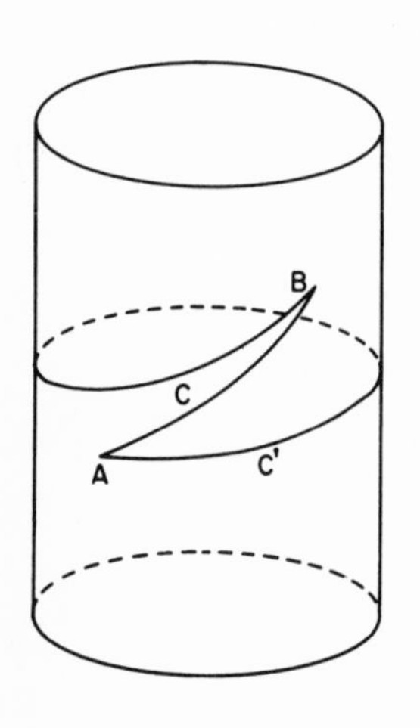

FIG. 1

Along any integral curve of (6.25) the condition

$$g_{ij} \frac{dx^i}{ds} \frac{dx^j}{ds} = \text{const.} \tag{6.30}$$

is satisfied. To show this we have merely to differentiate the left member of (6.30) and then eliminate the second derivatives d^2x^i/ds^2 by means of (6.25); the expression so obtained then vanishes identically on account of (6.26). The constant in the right member of (6.30) must be positive since the form (6.1) is positive definite by hypothesis. For a geodesic curve C, where s denotes the arc length measured from a fixed point A of C, the right member of (6.30) is of course equal to unity.

7. Affinely Connected Spaces

To obtain the equations of transformation of the Christoffel symbols Γ^i_{jk} let us first differentiate the relations (6.2) with respect to the coordinates x^k; this gives

$$\frac{\partial \bar{g}_{ij}}{\partial \bar{x}^k} = \frac{\partial g_{ab}}{\partial x^c}\frac{\partial x^a}{\partial \bar{x}^i}\frac{\partial x^b}{\partial \bar{x}^j}\frac{\partial x^c}{\partial \bar{x}^k} + g_{ab}\frac{\partial^2 x^a}{\partial \bar{x}^k \partial \bar{x}^i}\frac{\partial x^b}{\partial \bar{x}^j} + g_{ab}\frac{\partial x^a}{\partial \bar{x}^i}\frac{\partial^2 x^b}{\partial \bar{x}^k \partial \bar{x}^j}. \tag{7.1}$$

By cyclic permutation of the indices i, j, k in (7.1) we obtain

$$\frac{\partial \bar{g}_{jk}}{\partial \bar{x}^i} = \frac{\partial g_{ab}}{\partial x^c}\frac{\partial x^a}{\partial \bar{x}^j}\frac{\partial x^b}{\partial \bar{x}^k}\frac{\partial x^c}{\partial \bar{x}^i} + g_{ab}\frac{\partial^2 x^a}{\partial \bar{x}^i \partial \bar{x}^j}\frac{\partial x^b}{\partial \bar{x}^k} + g_{ab}\frac{\partial x^a}{\partial \bar{x}^j}\frac{\partial^2 x^b}{\partial \bar{x}^i \partial \bar{x}^k}. \tag{7.2}$$

$$\frac{\partial \bar{g}_{ki}}{\partial \bar{x}^j} = \frac{\partial g_{ab}}{\partial x^c}\frac{\partial x^a}{\partial \bar{x}^k}\frac{\partial x^b}{\partial \bar{x}^i}\frac{\partial x^c}{\partial \bar{x}^j} + g_{ab}\frac{\partial^2 x^a}{\partial \bar{x}^j \partial \bar{x}^k}\frac{\partial x^b}{\partial \bar{x}^i} + g_{ab}\frac{\partial x^a}{\partial \bar{x}^k}\frac{\partial^2 x^b}{\partial \bar{x}^j \partial \bar{x}^i}. \tag{7.3}$$

Now if we combine the three equations (7.1), (7.2) and (7.3) and take account of the symmetry of the second derivatives we are led to the following relations

$$\frac{1}{2}\left(\frac{\partial \bar{g}_{ij}}{\partial \bar{x}^k} + \frac{\partial \bar{g}_{jk}}{\partial \bar{x}^i} - \frac{\partial \bar{g}_{ki}}{\partial \bar{x}^j}\right) = g_{ab}\frac{\partial x^a}{\partial \bar{x}^j}\frac{\partial^2 x^b}{\partial \bar{x}^i \partial \bar{x}^k}$$
$$+ \frac{1}{2}\left(\frac{\partial g_{ab}}{\partial x^c} + \frac{\partial g_{bc}}{\partial x^a} - \frac{\partial g_{ca}}{\partial x^b}\right)\frac{\partial x^a}{\partial \bar{x}^i}\frac{\partial x^b}{\partial \bar{x}^j}\frac{\partial x^c}{\partial \bar{x}^k}.$$

Finally we multiply the two members of these latter equations by the corresponding members of the equations

$$\bar{g}^{jm}\frac{\partial x^p}{\partial \bar{x}^m} = g^{pq}\frac{\partial \bar{x}^j}{\partial x^q},$$

equivalent to (6.11), and sum on repeated indices the desired equations are obtained, namely

$$\bar{\Gamma}^m_{jk}\frac{\partial x^i}{\partial \bar{x}^m} = \frac{\partial^2 x^i}{\partial \bar{x}^j \partial \bar{x}^k} + \Gamma^i_{ab}\frac{\partial x^a}{\partial \bar{x}^j}\frac{\partial x^b}{\partial \bar{x}^k}, \tag{7.4}$$

where the Γ's are given by (6.26) and the $\bar{\Gamma}$'s by similar equations based on the components $\bar{g}_{ij}$ of the metric tensor relative to the $\bar{x}$ coordinate system.

From the above derivation it is evident that the equations (7.4) have the transitive property, i.e. if $\Gamma^i_{jk} \to \bar{\Gamma}^i_{jk}$ and $\bar{\Gamma}^i_{jk} \to \bar{\bar{\Gamma}}^i_{jk}$ by equations of the type (7.4) as the result of the successive coordinate transformations $x \leftrightarrow \bar{x}$ and $\bar{x} \leftrightarrow \bar{\bar{x}}$ then the elimination of the quantities $\bar{\Gamma}^i_{jk}$ between these two sets of equations will yield a set of equations of the type (7.4) relating the quantities Γ^i_{jk} and $\bar{\bar{\Gamma}}^i_{jk}$ relative to the x and $\bar{\bar{x}}$ coordinate systems. Hence we can consider a coordinate manifold of n dimensions such that (1) a definite set of functions Γ^i_{jk} of the coordinates, not necessarily Christoffel symbols, is defined in each of the allowable coordinate systems of the manifold and (2) the functions Γ^i_{jk} transform by the equations (7.4) under allowable transformations $x \leftrightarrow \bar{x}$ of the coordinates. The entity having the functions Γ^i_{jk} as its components in the allowable coordinate systems of the manifold is called an *affine connection* and a manifold over which such an affine connection is defined is called an *affinely connected space of n dimensions.* The affinely connected space will be said to be of class C^r if the components Γ^i_{jk} of the connection are of class C^r in the allowable coordinate systems covering the manifold. It will be assumed specifically that in an affinely connected space of class C^r the allowable coordinate transformations are of class C^{r+2} for $r \neq A$ and that the allowable coordinate transformations are of class C^A for an affinely connected space of class C^A (analytic affinely connected space) since these transformations preserve the class of the components Γ^i_{jk} without being unduly restricted (cp. Sect. 6).

In an affinely connected space one can consider the curves obtained as solutions of the system of differential equations (6.25). These curves, which constitute a generalization of the geodesics of a Riemann space, have been called *paths* and may be thought of as affording a means by which one can find his way about in a space with an affine connection. The body of theorems which state properties of the paths as defined by a particular set of parameterized equations (6.25) is called the *affine geometry of paths*. As an example of an affine property we may mention the following result. *If P is any point of an affinely connected space there exists a domain D containing P such that any two points P_1 and P_2 of D can be joined by one, and only one, path C lying in the domain D.* For a proof of this result the reader is referred to the original paper by J. H. C. Whitehead, *Convex regions in the geometry of paths*, Quart. Jour. of Math. 3 (1932), pp. 33 — 42.

8. Normal Coordinates

Consider the differential equations (6.25) which define the paths in an affinely connected space of class C^A. If we differentiate these equations successively we are lead to a sequence of equations which can be written in the following form

$$\frac{d^3x^i}{ds^3} + \Gamma^i_{jkm}\frac{dx^j}{ds}\frac{dx^k}{ds}\frac{dx^m}{ds} = 0,$$

$$\frac{d^4x^i}{ds^4} + \Gamma^i_{jkmr}\frac{dx^j}{ds}\frac{dx^k}{ds}\frac{dx^m}{ds}\frac{dx^r}{ds} = 0,$$

. . . .

. . . .

The coefficients Γ in these equations are given by the recurrence formula

$$\Gamma^i_{jk\ldots st} = \frac{1}{M} P\left[\frac{\partial \Gamma^i_{jk\ldots s}}{\partial x^t} - \Gamma^i_{ak\ldots s}\Gamma^a_{jt} - \ldots - \Gamma^i_{jk\ldots a}\Gamma^a_{st}\right],$$

where M denotes the number of subscripts $jk\ldots st$ and the symbol P denotes the sum of the terms obtainable from the one inside the bracketts by permuting the set of subscripts cyclically. As so defined the above functions Γ have the property of being unchanged by any permutation of the subscripts. The parametric equations $x^i = \phi^i(s)$ of a path C are determined by (6.25) and the above sequence of equations in conjunction with the initial conditions

$$x^i = p^i; \qquad \frac{dx^i}{ds} = \xi^i, \qquad \text{for} \qquad s = 0. \tag{8.1}$$

In fact we have

$$\phi^i(s) = p^i + \xi^i s - \frac{1}{2!}\Gamma^i_{jk}(p)\,\xi^j\xi^k s^2 - \frac{1}{3!}\Gamma^i_{jkm}(p)\,\xi^j\xi^k\xi^m s^3 - \ldots,$$

where the right members are convergent power series for sufficiently small values of s. A path C is therefore uniquely determined by the specification of a point P and a direction with components ξ^i at P. Putting $y^i = \xi^i s$ the above series becomes

$$x^i = p^i + y^i - \frac{1}{2!} \Gamma^i_{jk}(p)\, y^j y^k - \frac{1}{3!} \Gamma^i_{jkm}(p)\, y^j y^k y^m - \ldots, \tag{8.2}$$

and this series will converge in a domain D defined $|y^i| < a^i$, where the a's are sufficiently small positive constants. Since the Jacobian determinant of the right members of (8.2) is equal to 1 at the point P, the equations (8.2) can be solved so as to obtain

$$y^i = x^i - p^i + \Lambda^i(p, x - p),$$

where Λ^i is a multiple power series in $x^i - p^i$ beginning with second order terms. Hence (8.2) defines a coordinate transformation to a system of coordinates y^i such that the equations $y^i = \xi^i s$, where the ξ's are arbitrary constants, represent a path through the origin of the system, i.e. the point P; conversely any path through P can be represented in this way. The coordinates y^i are called *normal coordinates*. To any point Q with coordinates q^i in the domain D defined by $|y^i| < a^i$, a path can be drawn from the origin of the normal coordinate system. For example $y^i = q^i s$ are the equations of such a path and this path will lie entirely in the domain D; as is easily seen there is one, and only one, such path through the origin and the point Q.

The normal coordinates y^i are determined uniquely by the x coordinate system and a point P, this point being identified with the origin of the normal coordinate system. Let us now transform the coordinates x^i by an analytic transformation $x \leftrightarrow \bar{x}$ and let us then define the normal coordinates $\bar{y}^i$ which are determined by the $\bar{x}$ coordinate system and the above point P. We seek the analytical relation between the coordinates y^i and $\bar{y}^i$ of these two normal coordinate systems. Now by the transformation $x \leftrightarrow \bar{x}$ the equations $x^i = \phi^i(s)$ of a path C determined by the initial conditions (8.1) go over into the equations $\bar{x}^i = \psi^i(s)$ and the initial conditions (8.1) become

$$\bar{x}^i = \bar{p}^i; \qquad \frac{d\bar{x}^i}{ds} = \bar{\xi}^i, \qquad \text{for} \qquad s = 0,$$

where the $\bar{p}^i$ are the coordinates of the point P relative to the $\bar{x}$ system; also

$$\xi^i = a^i_k \, \bar{\xi}^k; \qquad a^i_k = \left(\frac{\partial x^i}{\partial \bar{x}^k}\right)_P. \tag{8.3}$$

Now $y^i = \xi^i s$ and $\bar{y}^i = \bar{\xi}^i s$ are respectively the equations of the path C with reference to the y and $\bar{y}$ normal coordinate systems. Hence if we multiply both members of the first set of equations (8.3) by the parameter s, we obtain

$$y^i = a^i_k \, \bar{y}^k, \tag{8.4}$$

along the path C. But any point Q in a sufficiently small neighborhood of P is joined to P by a unique path; hence the relation (8.4) holds throughout the neighborhood of the point P and we have the following result.

When the coordinates x^i undergo an analytic transformation $x \leftrightarrow \bar{x}$ the normal coordinates y^i determined by the x coordinate system and a point P suffer a linear homogeneous transformation (8.4) *with constant coefficients.* Thus the normal coordinates y^i are transformed like the components of a contravariant vector. They do not, however, define a vector in the narrow sense, but are the components of a "step" from the origin of the normal coordinates to the point having the coordinates y^i. An arbitrary step determined by the points P and Q can be represented by the coordinates of the point Q in a normal coordinate system associated with the point P, i.e. which has the point P as its origin.

There is an alternative method of treating normal coordinates which is of some interest. Let us suppose that the components $\Gamma^i_{jk}(x)$ become $C^i_{jk}(y)$ in the normal coordinate system, so that

$$C^m_{jk} \frac{\partial x^i}{\partial y^m} = \frac{\partial^2 x^i}{\partial y^j \, \partial y^k} + \Gamma^i_{ab} \frac{\partial x^a}{\partial y^j} \frac{\partial x^b}{\partial y^k} ; \tag{8.5}$$

The equations of the paths in normal coordinates will then be given by

$$\frac{d^2 y^i}{ds^2} + C^i_{jk} \frac{dy^j}{ds} \frac{dy^k}{ds} = 0. \tag{8.6}$$

Since the equations of a path through the origin are of the form $y^i = \xi^i s$, it follows from (8.6) that

$$C^i_{jk} \, \xi^j \, \xi^k = 0$$

all this path. Multiplying these latter equations through by s^2 we see that

$$C^i_{jk}(y) \, y^j \, y^k = 0, \tag{8.7}$$

and these equations must hold throughout the normal coordinate system since they are true along all paths through the origin; in other words *the equations* (8.7) *are satisfied identically in the normal coordinate system.*

Equations (8.7) can be used to define the normal coordinates y^i. From (8.5) and (8.7) we obtain

$$\left(\frac{\partial^2 x^i}{\partial y^j \, \partial y^k} + \Gamma^i_{ab} \frac{\partial x^a}{\partial y^j} \frac{\partial x^b}{\partial y^k} \right) y^j \, y^k = 0. \tag{8.8}$$

These differential equations uniquely determine a functional relation between the x^i and the y^i when taken in conjunction with the initial conditions

$$y^i = 0 \qquad \text{when} \qquad x^i = p^i,$$

$$\frac{\partial x^i}{\partial y^j} = \delta^i_j \qquad \text{when} \qquad x^i = p^i.$$

In fact if we differentiate (8.8) repeatedly and substitute these initial conditions, we obtain the equations (8.2), in which the Γ's have the values preciously determined.

To prove the relation (8.4) between the normal coordinates y^i and $\bar{y}^i$ as the result of their definition by means of the differential equations (8.8) we first construct the equations of transformation between the components C^i_{jk} and $\bar{C}^i_{jk}$ of the affine connection in these two normal coordinate systems, namely

$$\bar{C}^m_{jk} \frac{\partial y^i}{\partial \bar{y}^m} = \frac{\partial^2 y^i}{\partial \bar{y}^j \, \partial \bar{y}^k} + C^i_{ab} \frac{\partial y^a}{\partial \bar{y}^j} \frac{\partial y^b}{\partial \bar{y}^k} \cdot \tag{8.9}$$

Multiplying each side of (8.9) by $y^j y^k$ and summing on the indices j and k, we obtain

$$\left(\frac{\partial^2 y^j}{\partial \bar{y}^j \, \partial \bar{y}^k} + C^i_{ab} \frac{\partial y^a}{\partial \bar{y}^j} \frac{\partial y^b}{\partial \bar{y}^k} \right) y^j \, y^k = 0, \tag{8.10}$$

in consequence of the equations (8.7) with reference to the normal coordinates $\bar{y}^i$. By the definition of the normal coordinates the relation between the y^i and $\bar{y}^i$ must be such as to satisfy the conditions

$$y^i = 0; \qquad \frac{\partial y^i}{\partial \bar{y}^j} = a^i_j, \qquad \text{when} \qquad \bar{y}^i = 0, \tag{8.11}$$

where the constants a^i_j are defined by (8.3). The fact that (8.4) constitutes the relation between the normal coordinates y^i and $\bar{y}^i$ then follows by observing *first* that (8.4) satisfies (8.10) and the conditions (8.11) and *second* that (8.10) has a unique solution satisfying the conditions (8.11).

The equations (8.7) *characterize the coordinates* y^i *as normal coordinates,* i.e., *if* C^i_{jk} *are the components of affine connection in a system of coordinates* y^i, *assumed to have its origin* $y^i = 0$ *at some point P of the affine connected space, and if the equations* (8.7) *are satisfied identically, then the* y^i *are normal coordinates.* To see this let us determine the normal coordinate system $\hat{y}$ having its origin at the origin P of the y coordinate system. The normal coordinates $\hat{y}^i$ will then be given as solutions of the system of differential equations

$$\left(\frac{\partial^2 y^i}{\partial \hat{y}^j\, \partial \hat{y}^k} + C^i_{ab}\, \frac{\partial y^a}{\partial \hat{y}^j}\, \frac{\partial y^b}{\partial \hat{y}^k}\right) \hat{y}^j\, \hat{y}^k = 0,$$

subject to the initial conditions

$$y^i = 0; \qquad \frac{\partial y^i}{\partial \hat{y}^j} = \delta^i_j, \qquad \text{when} \qquad \hat{y}^i = 0.$$

Hence $y^i = \hat{y}^i$ since this satisfies the initial conditions and also the differential equations on account of (8.7); it follows that the y^i are normal coordinates.

Remark. Other equations besides (8.7) can be found which will characterize the normal coordinates y^i in the special case of a Riemann space; this circumstance arises from the fact that, for a Riemann space, the components Γ^i_{jk} are Christoffel symbols based on the quantities g_{ij}. Hence equations (8.7) reduce immediately to the equations

$$\left(2\, \frac{\partial \psi_{ij}}{\partial y^k} - \frac{\partial \psi_{jk}}{\partial y^i}\right) y^j\, y^k = 0, \tag{8.12}$$

where the ψ_{ij} denote the components of the fundamental metric tensor in the normal coordinates y^i. Now the relation (6.30), holding along any path of the space, implies the relation

$$\psi_{ij}\, \xi^i\, \xi^j = (\psi_{ij})_0\, \xi^i\, \xi^j \tag{8.13}$$

along a path C, defined by $y^i = \xi^i s$, through the origin of the normal coordinate system, where the $(\psi_{ij})_0$ are the values of the components ψ_{ij} at the origin of the normal coordinates; hence

$$\psi_{ij}\, y^i\, y^j = (\psi_{ij})_0\, y^i\, y^j \tag{8.14}$$

in the system of normal coordinates y^i. Differentiating (8.14) we obtain

$$\frac{\partial \psi_{jk}}{\partial y^i}\, y^j\, y^k + 2\, \psi_{ij}\, y^j - 2(\psi_{ij})_0\, y^j = 0,$$

and these equations, when combined with (8.12), yield

$$\frac{\partial \psi_{ij}}{\partial y^k}\, y^j\, y^k + \psi_{ij}\, y^j - (\psi_{ij})_0\, y^j = 0. \tag{8.15}$$

Now along the above path C we observe that

$$\frac{d}{ds}\left[\psi_{ij}\, y^j - (\psi_{ij})_0\, y^j\right] = 0,$$

in consequence of (8.15). Hence

$$\psi_{ij}\, y^j = (\psi_{ij})_0\, y^j, \tag{8.16}$$

since C is an arbitrary path through the origin of the normal coordinate system. *The equations* (8.16) *characterize the coordinates* y^i *as normal coordinates.* To prove this we have merely to differentiate (8.16) with respect to y^k and then multiply the resulting equations by y^k and y^i in turn. We thus find the two following sets of equations

$$\frac{\partial \psi_{ij}}{\partial y^k}\, y^j\, y^k = 0, \tag{8.17}$$

$$\frac{\partial \psi_{ij}}{\partial y^k}\, y^i\, y^j = 0. \tag{8.18}$$

But (8.17) and (8.18) imply (8.12) which characterize the y^i as normal coordinates.

It can be shown that *the coordinates* y^i *are likewise characterized as normal coordinates by the equations* (8.17). Observe that along the curve $y^i = \xi^i s$ we have

$$\frac{d}{ds}\left[\psi_{ij}\, \xi^j - (\psi_{ij})_0\, \xi^j\right] = \frac{\partial \psi_{ij}}{\partial y^k}\, \xi^j\, \xi^k = 0,$$

on account of (8.17). It readily follows from this result that (8.16) is satisfied in the y system and hence the y^i are normal coordinates. *Correspondingly the equations* (8.18) *characterize the* y^i *as normal coordinates.* Thus, using (8.18), we have

$$\frac{d}{ds}\left[\psi_{ij}\, \xi^i\, \xi^j - (\psi_{ij})_0\, \xi^i\, \xi^j\right] = \frac{\partial \psi_{ij}}{\partial y^k}\, \xi^i\, \xi^j\, \xi^k = 0,$$

along the curve $y^i = \xi^i s$. It follows that the bracket expression in this relation must vanish and hence

$$\psi_{ij}\, y^i\, y^j = (\psi_{ij})_0\, y^i\, y^j$$

in the y system. Differentiating this relation with respect to y^k and again making use of (8.18) we arrive at the identity (8.16) which proves the result.

9. General Theory of Extension

Let the relative tensor T of weight W have components $T^{i\ldots j}_{k\ldots m}(x)$ with reference to the coördinates x^i and the components $t^{i\ldots j}_{k\ldots m}(y)$ when referred to a system of normal coordinates y^i which are determined by the x coordinate system and a point P as origin. We shall show that

$$T^{i\ldots j}_{k\ldots m,r} = \left(\frac{\partial t^{i\ldots j}_{k\ldots m}}{\partial y^r}\right)_0, \tag{9.1}$$

where the derivatives are evaluated at the origin of normal coordinates, defines a set of functions $T^{i\ldots j}_{k\ldots m,r}(x)$ of the coordinates x^i which are the components of a relative tensor of weight W.

Denote by $\bar{t}^{p\ldots q}_{u\ldots v}(\bar{y})$ the components of the tensor T with respect to the normal coordinates $\bar{y}^i$ defined in Sect. 8; then we have

$$\bar{t}^{p\ldots q}_{u\ldots v} = |\partial y/\partial \bar{y}|^W \, t^{i\ldots j}_{k\ldots m} \frac{\partial \bar{y}^p}{\partial y^i} \cdots \frac{\partial \bar{y}^q}{\partial y^j} \frac{\partial y^k}{\partial \bar{y}^u} \cdots \frac{\partial y^m}{\partial \bar{y}^v}. \tag{9.2}$$

In view of (8.4) the derivatives in (9.2) are constants and hence

$$\frac{\partial \bar{t}^{p\ldots q}_{u\ldots v}}{\partial \bar{y}^w} = |\partial y/\partial \bar{y}|^W \frac{\partial t^{i\ldots j}_{k\ldots m}}{\partial y^r} \frac{\partial \bar{y}^p}{\partial y^i} \cdots \frac{\partial \bar{y}^q}{\partial y^j} \frac{\partial y^k}{\partial \bar{y}^u} \cdots \frac{\partial y^m}{\partial \bar{y}^v} \frac{\partial y^r}{\partial \bar{y}^w}.$$

Evaluating at the origin of normal coordinates we obtain

$$\bar{T}^{p\ldots q}_{u\ldots v,w} = |\partial x/\partial \bar{x}|^W \, T^{i\ldots j}_{k\ldots m,r} \frac{\partial \bar{x}^p}{\partial x^i} \cdots \frac{\partial \bar{x}^q}{\partial x^j} \frac{\partial x^k}{\partial \bar{x}^u} \cdots \frac{\partial x^m}{\partial \bar{x}^v} \frac{\partial x^r}{\partial \bar{x}^w}$$

which proves that the functions $T^{i\ldots j}_{k\ldots m,r}$ defined by (9.1) constitute the components of a relative tensor T_1 of weight W as above stated. This tensor is called the *first extension* or the *first covariant derivative* of the tensor T; the process of forming the first extension or first covariant derivative is referred to as *covariant differentiation.*

By repeated covariant differentiation one obtains the second and high covariant derivatives.

To construct the explixit formula involving the Γ's and their derivatives for the components of the tensor T_1 let us first observe that

$$\frac{\partial|\partial x/\partial y|^W}{\partial y^r} = W\,|\partial x/\partial y|^W \frac{\partial x^a}{\partial y^r\,\partial y^b}\,\frac{\partial y^b}{\partial x^a}, \tag{9.3}$$

from the well known process for the differentiation of a determinant. Hence, differentiating the equations

$$t^{i\ldots j}_{k\ldots m} = |\partial x/\partial y|^W\, T^{p\ldots q}_{u\ldots v}\frac{\partial x^u}{\partial y^k}\cdots\frac{\partial x^v}{\partial y^m}\,\frac{\partial y^i}{\partial x^p}\cdots\frac{\partial y^j}{\partial x^q}$$

with respect to y^r, using (8.2) and (9.3), and evaluating at the origin of normal coordinates, we obtain

$$\left.\begin{aligned} T^{i\ldots j}_{k\ldots m,r} = \frac{\partial T^{i\ldots j}_{k\ldots m}}{\partial x^r} - T^{i\ldots j}_{a\ldots m}\,\Gamma^a_{kr} - \ldots - T^{i\ldots j}_{k\ldots a}\,\Gamma^a_{mr} \\ + T^{a\ldots j}_{k\ldots m}\,\Gamma^i_{ar} + \ldots + T^{i\ldots a}_{k\ldots m}\,\Gamma^j_{ar} - W\,T^{i\ldots j}_{k\ldots m}\,\Gamma^a_{ar}, \end{aligned}\right\} \tag{9.4}$$

as the formula for the components of the tensor T_1.

In a similar manner we can show that the equations

$$T^{i\ldots j}_{k\ldots m,p\ldots q} = \left(\frac{\partial^r\, t^{i\ldots j}_{k\ldots m}}{\partial y^p\ldots\partial y^q}\right)_0, \tag{9.5}$$

define a set of functions $T^{i\ldots j}_{k\ldots m,p\ldots q}$ of the coordinates x^i which constitute the components of a relative tensor of weight W. This relative tensor will be called the rth *extension of the relative tensor* T provided the set $p\ldots q$ contains r indices. From the definition by means of the equations (9.5) we see that the components $T^{i\ldots j}_{k\ldots m,p\ldots q}$ are symmetric in the indices $p\ldots q$ added by the process of extension. Thus

$$T^{i\ldots j}_{k\ldots m,p\ldots q} = T^{i\ldots j}_{k\ldots m,u\ldots v},$$

where $u\ldots v$ denotes any permutation of the indices $p\ldots q$. In case $r=1$ this extension reverts to the covariant derivative previously considered.

The formula for the components of the extension of the sum of two relative tensors of the same kind or the product of any two relative tensors is analogous to the formula for the differentiation of the sum or product of two functions; this follows directly from the definition of these components by means of (9.5).

General formulae of extension can be calculated by the same process as that employed in the derivation of (9.4). The formula for the components $T^{i\ldots j}_{k\ldots m,p\ldots q}$ of the rth extension of the tensor T of weight $W \neq 0$ involves the formulae for the first r extensions of T considered as a tensor of weight zero. We have

$$t^{i\ldots j}_{k\ldots m} = |\partial x/\partial y|^W f^{i\ldots j}_{k\ldots m}, \tag{9.6}$$

where

$$f^{i\ldots j}_{k\ldots m} = T^{p\ldots q}_{u\ldots v} \frac{\partial x^u}{\partial y^k} \cdots \frac{\partial x^v}{\partial y^m} \frac{\partial y^i}{\partial x^p} \cdots \frac{\partial y^j}{\partial x^q}.$$

Differentiating (9.6) and evaluating at the origin of normal coordinates, we obtain

$$\left.\begin{aligned} T^{i\ldots j}_{k\ldots m,pa\ldots bq} = T^{i\ldots j}_{k\ldots m/pa\ldots bq} + S(\Delta^W_p T^{i\ldots j}_{k\ldots m/a\ldots bq}) + \cdots \\ + S(\Delta^W_{pa\ldots b} T^{i\ldots j}_{k\ldots m/q}) + \Delta^W_{pa\ldots bq} T^{i\ldots j}_{k\ldots m}, \end{aligned}\right\} \tag{9.7}$$

where

$$T^{i\ldots j}_{k\ldots m/r\ldots s} = \left(\frac{\partial^m f^{i\ldots j}_{k\ldots m}}{\partial y^r \ldots \partial y^s}\right)_0; \qquad \Delta^W_{r\ldots s} = \left[\frac{\partial^m \log|\partial x/\partial y|^W}{\partial y^r \ldots \partial y^s}\right]_0,$$

and $S(\ )$ denotes the sum of the different terms obtainable from the one in parenthesis by forming arbitrary combinations of the subscripts $pa\ldots bq$ which are distinct when account is taken of the symmetry in the added indices of differentiation. The expression for $T^{i\ldots j}_{k\ldots m/r\ldots s}$, where there are m indices in the set $r\ldots s$, is given by the formula for the mth extension of a tensor of weight zero having the components $T^{i\ldots j}_{k\ldots m}$; these expressions do not in general constitute the components of a tensor for the case under consideration. The quantities $\Delta^W_{r\ldots s}$ have the values

$$\Delta^W_r = -W\Gamma^i_{ir},$$

$$\Delta^W_{rs} = -W\Gamma^i_{irs} + W\Gamma^i_{jr}\Gamma^j_{is} + W^2\Gamma^i_{ir}\Gamma^j_{js},$$

$$\ldots\ldots\ldots\ldots\ldots\ldots\ldots\ldots\ldots\ldots$$

$$\ldots\ldots\ldots\ldots\ldots\ldots\ldots\ldots\ldots\ldots$$

in which the Γ^i_{jkm}, etc. are the functions of the Γ^i_{jk} and their derivatives defined in Sect. 8.

The formula for the components of any extension of a relative tensor T of weight W may be obtained by substituting the proper values of $T^{i\ldots j}_{k\ldots m|r\ldots s}$ and $\Delta^W_{r\ldots s}$ into (9.7). Thus we may write

$$T^{i\ldots j}_{k\ldots m,p} = T^{i\ldots j}_{k\ldots m|p} - WT^{i\ldots j}_{k\ldots m}\Gamma^a_{ap},$$

in place of the formula (9.4). In the following remarks we have given a few examples of formulae of covariant differentiation which are of frequent occurrence in the geometrical and physical applications of this theory.

Remark 1. As special formulae of covariant differentiation we have

$$V_{i,j} = \frac{\partial V_i}{\partial x^j} - V_m \Gamma^m_{ij}; \qquad V^i_{,j} = \frac{\partial V^i}{\partial x^j} + V^m \Gamma^i_{mj}, \tag{9.8}$$

according as V is a covariant or a contravariant vector. Also

$$V_{i,j,k} = \frac{\partial V_{i,j}}{\partial x^k} - V_{m,j}\Gamma^m_{ik} - V_{i,m}\Gamma^m_{jk}, \tag{9.9}$$

$$V_{i,jk} = \frac{\partial^2 V_i}{\partial x^j\,\partial x^k} - \frac{\partial V_i}{\partial x^m}\Gamma^m_{jk} - \left(\frac{\partial V_m}{\partial x^j}\Gamma^m_{ik} + \frac{\partial V_m}{\partial x^k}\Gamma^m_{ij}\right) - V_m\Gamma^m_{ijk}. \tag{9.10}$$

The formula (9.9) gives the components of the second covariant derivative of a covariant vector V and is not, in general, identical with the second extension of V whose components are given by (9.10) for comparison.

If σ is a covariant tensor of the second order the formula for the components of its covariant derivative is

$$\sigma_{ij,k} = \frac{\partial \sigma_{ij}}{\partial x^k} - \sigma_{mj}\,\Gamma^m_{ik} - \sigma_{im}\,\Gamma^m_{jk}. \tag{9.11}$$

In the case of a Riemann space for which the Γ's are Christoffel symbols defined by (6.26) it follows readily from (9.11) that $g_{ij,k} = 0$, i.e. *the components of the covariant derivative of the fundamental metric tensor of a Riemann space are equal to zero.* This fact can also be inferred by differentiating the identities (8.18) with respect to the coordinates y^p and y^q and then evaluating the resulting equations at the origin of the normal coordinate system. By covariant differentiation of (6.8) and use of the condition $g_{ij,k} = 0$ we can immediately deduce the vanishing of the components of the covariant derivative of the contravariant form of the metric tensor. In this connection we may also observe the vanishing of the components of the covariant derivative of the relative scalar defined by $\sqrt{g}$ in an oriented Riemann space.

Remark 2. If we contract the indices i and j in the second formula (9.8) we obtain the scalar quantity

$$V^i_{,i} = \frac{\partial V^i}{\partial x^i} + V^m\,\Gamma^i_{im}. \tag{9.12}$$

This scalar is known as the divergence of the vector V. By raising the index on the symbol of a covariant vector in a Riemann space the formula (9.12) can be applied to give the divergence of such a vector. Thus the divergence of a covariant vector V in a Riemann space is the scalar defined by

$$(g^{ij}\,V_i)_{,j} = g^{ij}\,V_{i,j} = g^{ij}\frac{\partial V_i}{\partial x^i} - V_m\,g^{ij}\,\Gamma^m_{ij}. \tag{9.13}$$

There is an interesting result which can be derived from (9.4) for the case where T is a contravariant vector of weight 1; denoting the components of this vector by W^i, we have

$$W^i_{,j} = \frac{\partial W^i}{\partial x^j} + W^m\,\Gamma^i_{mj} - W^i\,\Gamma^m_{mj}.$$

Hence

$$W^i_{,i} = \frac{\partial W^i}{\partial x^i}, \tag{9.14}$$

i.e. the sum of the partial derivatives appearing in the right member of (9.14) is a relative scalar of weight 1. It follows immediately from this result and the result in Remark 1 regarding the vanishing of the covariant derivative of the metric tensor and the covariant derivative of the relative scalar $\sqrt{g}$ of an oriented Riemann space that the quantity

$$\sqrt{g}\, g^{ij}\, V_{i,j} = (\sqrt{g}\, g^{ij}\, V_i)_{,j} = \frac{\partial(\sqrt{g}\, g^{ij}\, V_i)}{\partial x^j},$$

defines a relative scalar of weight 1 in the oriented space provided the V_i are the components of a covariant vector.

Remark 3. For the purpose of defining the normal coordinate system on which the above theory of covariant differentiation and extension of tensors is based we have assumed the analyticity of the components of affine connection Γ^i_{jk} and of the allowable coordinate transformations. It is now perhaps not without interest to observe that this strong condition of analyticity is unnecessary for the formal results of this section. In fact it is easily seen that the formulae which we have derived for the components of the covariant derivatives and extensions of a tensor T will possess the required tensorial character provided only that the operations of differentiation involved in the formulae can be carried out so that the components in question can be defined in the various allowable coordinate systems within the affinely connected space. Thus it is sufficient for the quantities $V_{i,j}$ or $V^i_{,j}$ given by (9.8) to be the components of a tensor that the vector V be of class C^1, i.e. that the components V_i or V^i be continuous and have continuous first partial derivatives in the allowable coordinate systems, and that the affinely connected space be of class C^0 (see Sect. 7).

10. Absolute Differentiation

Let C be a parameterized curve defined by $x^i = \phi^i(s)$ in an affinely connected space and regular in the sense that the functions $\phi^i(s)$ possess continuous derivatives which do not all vanish for any value of the parameter s (see Sect. 6). Let T be a tensor of weight W defined along C, i.e. specifically we regard the components $T^{i\ldots j}_{k\ldots m}$ of T as functions of the parameter s of the curve C. We shall say that the curve C or the tensor T is of class C^r if the functions $\phi^i(s)$ or the components $T^{i\ldots j}_{k\ldots m}(s)$ possess continuous derivatives with respect to s to the order r inclusive in the allowable coordinate systems of the space and it will be assumed, without further mention, that the class of the curve C and the tensor T is such that we can perform the operations of differentiation involved in the following discussion.

Now choose a point P on C and consider the normal coordinate system y which is determined by the point P, i.e. P is the origin of the normal system, and the x coordinate system (assumed to contain the point P). Denote the components of T by $t^{i\ldots j}_{k\ldots m}(s)$ in the y coordinate system. Then the equations

$$\frac{DT^{i\ldots j}_{k\ldots m}}{Ds} = \left(\frac{dt^{i\ldots j}_{k\ldots m}}{ds}\right)_{y=0}, \tag{10.1}$$

will define a set of functions $DT^{i\ldots j}_{k\ldots m}/Ds$ of the parameter s, relative to the x system, and these functions can be shown to be the components of a tensor of weight W under the allowable coordinate transformations of the space. In fact if we differentiate the equations (9.2), which give the relations between the components of the tensor T in the normal system y and the normal system $\bar{y}$, defined in Sect. 8, with respect to the parameter s and then evaluate at the origin in accordance with the equations (10.1), we obtain

$$\frac{D\bar{T}^{p\ldots q}_{u\ldots v}}{Ds} = |\partial x/\partial \bar{x}|^W \frac{DT^{i\ldots j}_{k\ldots m}}{Ds} \frac{\partial \bar{x}^p}{\partial x^i} \cdots \frac{\partial x^m}{\partial \bar{x}^v}.$$

The tensor of weight W having the quantities $DT^{i\ldots j}_{k\ldots m}/Ds$ as its components will be called the *absolute derivative* of the tensor T. By repeated application of this process of absolute differentiation we obtain the second absolute derivative, the third absolute derivative, ... with components which may be denoted by

$$\frac{D}{Ds}\left(\frac{DT^{i\ldots j}_{k\ldots m}}{Ds}\right); \qquad \frac{D}{Ds}\left[\frac{D}{Ds}\left(\frac{DT^{i\ldots j}_{k\ldots m}}{Ds}\right)\right]; \qquad \ldots .$$

The derivation of the formula for the components of the absolute derivative is analogous to the derivation of the relations (9.4), which give the components of the covariant derivative of a tensor, and consists in the differentiation of the transformation equations relating the components of the tensor T, relative to the x and y coordinate systems, with respect to the parameter s and then evaluating the equations obtained at the origin of the normal system. We thus deduce

$$\left.\begin{aligned} \frac{DT^{i\ldots j}_{k\ldots m}}{Ds} &= \frac{dT^{i\ldots j}_{k\ldots m}}{ds} - W\, T^{i\ldots j}_{k\ldots m} \Gamma^a_{ar} \frac{dx^r}{ds} \\ &\quad - (T^{i\ldots j}_{a\ldots m} \Gamma^a_{kr} + \ldots + T^{i\ldots j}_{k\ldots a} \Gamma^a_{mr}) \frac{dx^r}{ds} \\ &\quad + (T^{a\ldots j}_{k\ldots m} \Gamma^i_{ar} + \ldots + T^{i\ldots a}_{k\ldots m} \Gamma^j_{ar}) \frac{dx^r}{ds}, \end{aligned}\right\} \tag{10.2}$$

in which the derivatives dx^r/ds are obtained by differentiation of the parametric equations giving the curve C.

Correspondingly the quantities $D^r T^{i\ldots j}_{k\ldots m}/Ds^r$ defined by

$$\frac{D^r T^{i\ldots j}_{k\ldots m}}{Ds^r} = \left(\frac{d^r t^{i\ldots j}_{k\ldots m}}{ds^r}\right)_{y=0}, \tag{10.3}$$

can be shown to be the components of a relative tensor of weight W along the curve C; this tensor is called the rth *absolute extension* of the tensor T and a general formula for its components can be constructed analogous to the formula for the components of the rth extension of the tensor T in Sect. 9.

Remark. Vectors ξ defined along a parameterized curve C are said to be *parallel* with respect to the curve C if the absolute derivative of ξ vanishes along C. If ξ is a contravariant vector it follows from (10.2) that the condition for parallelism is

$$\frac{D\xi^i}{Ds} = \frac{d\xi^i}{ds} + \Gamma^i_{ar}\,\xi^a\,\frac{dx^r}{ds} = 0. \tag{10.4}$$

Now a solution $\xi^i(s)$ of the differential equations (10.4) is uniquely determined by the initial conditions $\xi^i = \xi^i_0$ for $s = s_0$; accordingly the vector ξ having the solution functions $\xi^i(s)$ as its components along the curve C is said to be obtained from the initial vector ξ_0 with components ξ^i_0 by *parallel displacement* along C.

The quantities dx^i/ds are the components of a contravariant vector along the curve C; this vector is said to be *tangent* to C. Putting $\xi^i = dx^i/ds$ in (10.4) we now have

$$\frac{d^2x^i}{ds^2} + \Gamma^i_{jk}\,\frac{dx^j}{ds}\,\frac{dx^k}{ds} = 0. \tag{10.5}$$

But these equations are identical with the equations which define the paths of an affinely connected space (see Sect. 7). Hence the tangent vectors are parallel with respect to the path. One may also express this result by saying that the paths of an affinely connected space can be generated by the continuous parallel displacement of a vector in its own direction.

11. Differential Invariants

In the further development of the theory of affinely connected spaces one is concerned with the determination of scalars and tensors whose components depend on the fundamental functions Γ^i_{jk} and their derivatives to a specified order. Such scalars or tensors are called *affine differential invariants* in the sense of the following definition.

A tensor T will be called an affine differential invariant of order r if its components

$$T^{i\ldots j}_{k\ldots m}\left(\Gamma^a_{bc}; \frac{\partial \Gamma^a_{bc}}{\partial x^p}; \ldots; \frac{\partial^r \Gamma^a_{bc}}{\partial x^p \ldots \partial x^q}\right)$$

are functions of the Γ's and their derivatives to the rth order, such that each component retains its form as a function of the Γ's and their derivatives under allowable coordinate transformations in the affinely connected space. Replacing the tensor law of transformation involved in this definition by other equations of transformation possessing the required property of transitivity, we are led to the concept of differential invariants which generalize the affine tensor differential invariants. Thus the quantities Γ^i_{jk} themselves are the components of a non-tensor differential invariant of order zero, i.e. *the affine connection.*

In the case of the Riemann space we are concerned with invariants in the general sense of the affine differential invariants except that the components of the invariants in question depend on the g_{ij} and their derivatives; if the components of the invariant involve derivatives of the g_{ij} up to and including those of order r ($\geqslant 0$), the invariant will be called a *metric differential invariant of order r.* As an example of such an invariant we have the *fundamental metric tensor* with components g_{ij}. Another example is furnished by the quantities g^{ij}, defined by (6.7), which are the components of the contravariant form of the fundamental metric tensor. The Christoffel symbols given by (6.26) constitute the components of a non-tensor differential invariant of order 1, i.e. the affine connection of this space.

If we differentiate (8.7) twice and then evaluate at the origin of normal coordinates, we obtain

$$C^i_{jk}(0) = 0, \tag{11.1}$$

i.e. *the components of affine connection C^i_{jk} in a system of normal coordinates vanish at the origin of the system.* Hence the power series expansion for the components C^i_{jk} about the origin of normal coordinate takes the form

$$C^i_{jk} = A^i_{jkp}\, y^p + \frac{1}{2!} A^i_{jkpq}\, y^p\, y^q + \dots, \tag{11.2}$$

in which the A's are the derivatives of C^i_{jk} evaluated at the origin, i.e.

$$A^i_{jkp\dots r} = \left(\frac{\partial^m C^i_{jk}}{\partial y^p \dots \partial y^r} \right)_0 . \tag{11.3}$$

The equations (11.3) can be taken to define the $A^i_{jkp\dots r}$ as a set of functions of the coordinates x^i of the origin P of the normal coordinate system corresponding to the definition of the extension of a tensor by means of normal coordinates (see Sect. 9). The functions $A^i_{jkp\dots r}$ so defined are the components of a tensor. To prove this we consider the transformation equations (8.9) in which the first derivatives are constants, and the second derivatives accordingly vanish, on account of the linearity of the relations (8.4). Repeated differentiation of (8.9), followed by evaluation at the origin of normal coordinates, then gives

$$\bar{A}^m_{jkp\dots r} \frac{\partial x^i}{\partial \bar{x}^m} = A^i_{abc\dots e} \frac{\partial x^a}{\partial \bar{x}^j} \frac{\partial x^b}{\partial \bar{x}^k} \frac{\partial x^c}{\partial \bar{x}^p} \cdots \frac{\partial x^e}{\partial \bar{x}^r}, \tag{11.4}$$

when use is made of the second set of equations (8.3); the tensor character of the quantities $A^i_{jkp\ldots r}$ follows from (11.4). We call these tensors the *affine normal tensors* on account of their definition in terms of the components of affine connection in normal coordinates.

The components of the affine normal tensors A are expressible in terms of the Γ^i_{jk} and their derivatives; *on this account these tensors become, by definition, tensor differential invariants of the affinely connected space.* If we differentiate the equations (8.5) and then substitute the values of the partial derivatives of the x^i with respect to the y's at the origin of normal coordinates, as computed from (8.2), we find

$$A^i_{jkm} = \frac{\partial \Gamma^i_{jk}}{\partial x^m} - \Gamma^i_{jkm} - \Gamma^i_{rk}\,\Gamma^r_{jm} - \Gamma^i_{jr}\,\Gamma^r_{km}. \tag{11.5}$$

It is evident that a continuation of this process, i.e. repeated differentiation of (8.5) followed by evaluation at the origin of normal coordinates, will determine the explicit formula for the components of any other affine normal tensor A.

In an analogous manner we can define an infinite set of tensor differential invariants, called *metric normal tensors*, whose components $g_{ij,k\ldots m}$ are given as functions of the coordinates x^i by the equations

$$g_{ij,k\ldots m} = \left(\frac{\partial^r \psi_{ij}}{\partial y^k \ldots \partial y^m}\right)_0, \tag{11.6}$$

where $\psi_{ij}(y)$ denotes the components of the fundamental metric tensor of a Riemann space in the system of normal coordinates as in the Remark in Sect. 8. The method of Sect. 9 can be applied to show that the quantities $g_{ij,k\ldots m}$ defined by (11.6) enjoy the tensor law of transformation, namely

$$\bar{g}_{ij,k\ldots m} = g_{ab,c\ldots e} \frac{\partial x^a}{\partial \bar{x}^i} \cdots \frac{\partial x^e}{\partial \bar{x}^m},$$

and also to deduce the explicit formula for these quantities. The first metric normal tensor having the components $g_{ij,k}$ is identical with the covariant derivative of the fundamental metric tensor and vanishes as we observed in the Remark 1 of Sect. 9. The formula for the components of the second metric normal tensor is

$$\left.\begin{aligned} g_{ij,km} = {} & \frac{\partial^2 g_{ij}}{\partial x^k \partial x^m} - g_{rj}\,\Gamma^r_{ikm} - g_{ir}\,\Gamma^r_{jkm} - \frac{\partial g_{ij}}{\partial x^r}\,\Gamma^r_{km} \\ & - \frac{\partial g_{rj}}{\partial x^k}\,\Gamma^r_{im} - \frac{\partial g_{ir}}{\partial x^k}\,\Gamma^r_{jm} - \frac{\partial g_{rj}}{\partial x^m}\,\Gamma^m_{im} - \frac{\partial g_{ir}}{\partial x^m}\,\Gamma^r_{jk} \\ & + g_{rs}\,(\Gamma^i_{rk}\,\Gamma^s_{jm} + \Gamma^r_{im}\,\Gamma^s_{jk}), \end{aligned}\right\} \quad (11.7)$$

and is obtained by two fold differentiation of the tensor equations relating the components g_{ij} and ψ_{ij} and then evaluating at the origin of the normal coordinate system. By a continuation of this procedure we can evidently construct the explicit formula for the components of any metric normal tensor.

Remark 1. The tensor differential invariant B whose components are given by

$$B^i_{jkm} = A^i_{jkm} - A^i_{jmk}, \quad (11.8)$$

can be identified with the well known curvature tensor of an affinely connected or a Riemann space. Substituting the values of the A's given by (11.5) into the equations (11.8) we obtain the explicit formula for the components of the tensor B in terms of the Γ^i_{jk} and their first derivatives; thus we find that

$$B^i_{jkm} = \frac{\partial \Gamma^i_{jk}}{\partial x^m} - \frac{\partial \Gamma^i_{jm}}{\partial x^k} + \Gamma^i_{am}\,\Gamma^a_{jk} - \Gamma^i_{ak}\,\Gamma^a_{jm}.$$

In the Riemann space this differential invariant admits a completely covariant form having the components

$$B_{ijkm} = g_{ir}\,B^r_{jkm}. \quad (11.9)$$

Remark 2. From the symmetry of the quantities Γ^i_{jk} in the indices j,k and from the definition of the affine normal tensors by the equations (11.3) it is seen that the components of any normal tensor A are symmetric in their first two subscripts and also in the remaining ones, i.e.

$$A^i_{jkp\ldots r} = A^i_{kjp\ldots r}; \qquad A^i_{jkp\ldots r} = A^i_{jkq\ldots s}, \quad (11.10)$$

where $q\ldots s$ denotes any permutation of the indices $p\ldots r$. Another set of identities involving the components $A^i_{jkp\ldots r}$ is obtained if we multiply both members of (11.2) by $y^j y^k$, sum on the repeated indices j and k, and then take account of the relations (8.7). Thus we see that

$$S(A^i_{jkp\ldots r}) = 0, \tag{11.11}$$

where S denotes the sum of the terms, not identical because of the symmetry relations (11.10), which are obtainable by permutation of the indices $jkp\ldots r$ from the one in the parenthesis.

It is seen immediately from the equations of definition (11.6) of the components of the metric normal tensors that we have

$$g_{ij,k\ldots m} = g_{ji,k\ldots m}; \qquad g_{ij,k\ldots m} = g_{ij,p\ldots q}, \tag{11.12}$$

where $p\ldots q$ denotes any permutation of the indices $k\ldots m$. To derive other identities satisfied by these components we have recourse to the equations (8.17). By repeated differentiation of (8.17), followed by evaluation at the origin of the normal coordinate system, we find that in addition to (11.12) we have the identities

$$S^*(g_{ij,k\ldots m}) = 0, \tag{11.13}$$

where S^* denotes the sum of all the terms which can be formed from the one in the parenthesis by permuting the indices $jk\ldots m$ cyclically.

In particular let us observe that the above relations give

$$A^i_{jkm} = A^i_{kjm}; \qquad A^i_{jkm} + A^i_{kmj} + A^i_{mjk} = 0, \tag{11.14}$$

and

$$\left.\begin{aligned} g_{ij,km} &= g_{ji,km} = g_{ij,mk}, \\ g_{ij,km} &+ g_{ik,mj} + g_{im,jk} = 0, \end{aligned}\right\} \tag{11.15}$$

as the identities satisfied by the components of the first affine normal tensor and the second metric normal tensor respectively. Corresponding to these identities there are the identities satisfied by the components of the curvature tensor B introduced in Remark 1, namely

$$B^i_{jkm} = -B^i_{jmk}; \qquad B^i_{jkm} + B^i_{kmj} + B^i_{mjk} = 0, \tag{11.16}$$

and

$$\left.\begin{aligned} B_{ijkm} &= -B_{jikm} = -B_{ijmk}, \\ B_{ijkm} &+ B_{ikmj} + B_{imjk} = 0. \end{aligned}\right\} \tag{11.17}$$

The identity (11.16) can be verified by replacing the B^i_{jkm} by the values given by (11.8) and then taking account of the identities (11.14). To verify (11.17) it will be helpful if one first deduces the relations

$$B_{ijkm} = g_{ik,jm} - g_{jk,im} \tag{11.18}$$

which can be obtained if we express the quantities B^r_{jkm} in terms of the g_{ij} and their first and second derivatives and then evaluate the equations (11.9) at the origin of a system of normal coordinates. Substitution of the values of the B_{ijkm} given by (11.18) into (11.17) then leads to the verification of these identities.

Remark 3. *A complete set of identities of the components of an invariant is a set of identities furnishing all the algebraic conditions on these components*; hence every identity satisfied by the components of the invariant can be deduced from the identities of the complete set by algebraic processes. For example, the components g_{ij} of the fundamental metric tensor of a Riemann space satisfy the symmetry identities

$$g_{ij} = g_{ji}. \tag{11.19}$$

These relations constitute a complete set of identities of the components g_{ij} since at an arbitrary point P of the general Riemann space the compc nents g_{ij} are obviously subject only to the conditions (11.19). Similarly the identities

$$\Gamma^i_{jk} = \Gamma^i_{kj}$$

are a complete set of identities of the components of affine connection of an affinely connected space. It can be shown that the identities (11.10) and (11.11) are a complete set of identities for the components $A^i_{jkp\ldots r}$; likewise a complete set of identities for the components $g_{ij,k\ldots m}$ is furnished by the relations (11.12) and (11.13). In particular the identities (11.14) and (11.15) are complete sets of identities for the components of the first affine normal tensor and the second metric normal tensor. Finally (11.16) and (11.17) give complete sets of identities for the components of the curvature tensor of an affinely connected space and Riemann space respectively.

For a proof of the above and other results on complete sets of identities and for a discussion of the various applications of the theory of differential invariants the reader is referred to the literature of this subject.

12. Transformation Groups

We observed in Sect. 1 that the coordinate transformations of a simple coordinate manifold of class C^u form a group whose elements, i.e. coordinate transformations, can be interpreted as (1,1) transformations of the arithmetic space of n dimensions into itself. By specializing this group, more precisely by limiting our attention to certain of its subgroups, we arrive at various well known spaces, among these being the Euclidean metric space with which we shall be concerned in much of the following discussion in this book. In order to consider this problem in the proper perspective let us denote by G a set of (1,1) transformations of the arithmetic space of n dimensions into itself and let us write down the following axioms in which the undefined elements are *points* and *preferred coordinate systems*. These axioms are:

G_1. *Each preferred coordinate system is a* (1,1) *transformation of the points into the arithmetic space of n dimensions,*

G_2. *Any transformation of coordinates from one preferred coordinate system to another belongs to G,*

G_3. *Any coordinate system obtained from a preferred coordinate system by a transformation belonging to G is preferred,*

G_4. *There exists at least one preferred coordinate system.*

Examining the consequences of the above axioms we see from G_1 that if $P \leftrightarrow (x^1,\ldots,x^n)$ and $P \leftrightarrow (y^1,\ldots,y^n)$ are two preferred coordinate systems there is a unique transformation $(x^1,\ldots,x^n) \leftrightarrow (y^1,\ldots,y^n)$ relating the coordinates of these systems; it follows from G_2 that this transformation belongs to the set G. Also if we select any preferred coordinate system, the existence of which is specified by G_4, it follows from the axioms G_1, G_2 and G_3

that the preferred coordinate systems are those, and only those, obtainable from the selected system by transformations belonging to G. Finally it is easily seen that the set of transformations G constitutes a group.

The underlying point set together with the set of preferred coordinate systems will be spoken of as a *space*. By the *geometry* of the space we mean the theory or body of theorems deducible from the above axioms $G_1, \ldots G_4$. If the group G is the group of all (1,1) transformations of class C^u of the n dimensional arithmetic space into itself, the space is identical with the simple coordinate manifold of class C^u discussed in Sect. 1. We now consider several groups G which lead to well known mathematical spaces. These groups are defined by their representative transformations as follows

$$\bar{x}^i = a^i_j x^j + b^i; \quad |a^i_j| \neq 0, \qquad (\textit{affine group}), \tag{12.1}$$

$$\bar{x}^i = a^i_j x^j + b^i; \quad a^i_j a^i_k = \delta_{jk}, \qquad (\textit{orthogonal group}), \tag{12.2}$$

$$\bar{x}^i = a^i_j x^j + b^i; \quad a^i_j a^i_k = \rho\delta_{jk}; \quad \rho > 0, \quad (\textit{Euclidean group}), \tag{12.3}$$

where there is a summation over the range $1, \ldots, n$ on all repeated indices and the quantities δ_{jk} are the Kronecker symbols previously defined and denoted by δ^i_k in Sect. 1. The coefficients ρ, b^i and a^i_j in the above equations are constants. In the case of the orthogonal and Euclidean groups we see from the conditions imposed on the constants a^i_j by the relations (12.2) and (12.3) that the determinant $|a^i_j|$ must be different from zero; however it must be assumed explicitly that the determinant $|a^i_j|$ does not vanish in the case of the affine group in order for (12.1) to represent a (1,1) coordinate transformation.

If G is the affine group the resulting space is called the *affine space* of n dimensions. We obtain the *Euclidean metric space* or the *Euclidean space* of n dimensions according as G is the orthogonal group or the Euclidean group. The preferred coordinate systems for the affine space are called *cartesian coordinate systems*; the preferred coordinate systems are called *rectangular cartesian coordinate systems*, or simply *rectangular coordinate systems* for brevity, in the Euclidean metric space and in the Euclidean space. By *affine geometry* we mean the theory of the affine space and by the *Euclidean metric geometry* and the *Euclidean geometry* we mean the theory of the Euclidean metric space and the Euclidean space respectively.

As explained for the case of the simple coordinate manifold of class C^u in Sect. 1 each of the above spaces will determine two *oriented spaces* for which the preferred coordinate systems are related by transformations whose functional determinants are positive. Thus an affine space determines two *oriented affine spaces* having preferred coordinate systems related by transformations (12.1) with $|a^i_j| > 0$; these restricted transformations (12.1) obviously determine a group which will be called the *proper affine group*. Correspondingly the preferred coordinate systems of an *oriented Euclidean metric space* and an *oriented Euclidean space* will be related by transformations of the *proper orthogonal group* and the *proper Euclidean group* defined by (12.2) and (12.3) respectively with $|a^i_j| > 0$; we observe in this connection that $|a^i_j| = \pm 1$ from the second set of relations (12.2) and hence $|a^i_j| = 1$ if (12.2) is to represent a proper orthogonal transformation.

The affine, Euclidean metric and Euclidean spaces, as well as the oriented spaces which they determine, are characterized essentially by the group G of coordinate transformations relating their preferred coordinate systems. Interpreting the transformations of the group G as point transformations, rather than coordinate transformations in the strict sense, let us say that two configurations (sets of points) in the space are *equivalent* if one can be transformed into the other by a transformation of G. In particular equivalent configurations in an oriented Euclidean metric space are said to be *congruent*; equivalent configurations are called *similar* in an oriented Euclidean space. Thus the ordinary concepts of congruence and similarity are given a precise meaning in terms of the transformations of a group.

13. Euclidean Metric Space

Let P_1 and P_2 be two points in a Euclidean metric space and denote by x_1^i and x_2^i respectively the coordinates of these points in a preferred or rectangular coordinate system. Now consider the expression

$$(x_1^i - x_2^i)(x_1^i - x_2^i), \tag{13.1}$$

where the index i is summed over the values $1, \ldots, n$. *The expression* (13.1) *is a scalar function of the points* P_1 *and* P_2. To show this fact let $\bar{x}_1^i$ and $\bar{x}_2^i$ be the coordinates of P_1 and P_2 in any other rectangular coordinate system. Then we have

$$(\bar{x}_1^i - \bar{x}_2^i)(\bar{x}_1^i - \bar{x}_2^i) = a_j^i a_k^i (x_1^j - x_2^j)(x_1^k - x_2^k),$$

when we make the substitution (12.2). But from the second set of relations (12.2) the above equations become

$$(\bar{x}_1^i - \bar{x}_2^i)(\bar{x}_1^i - \bar{x}_2^i) = \delta_{jk}(x_1^j - x_2^j)(x_1^k - x_2^k) = (x_1^i - x_2^i)(x_1^i - x_2^i),$$

which proves the scalar character of (13.1). *The scalar represented by* (13.1) *defines the square of the distance between the points* P_1 *and* P_2 *in the Euclidean metric space.* A similar determination of distance independently of the preferred coordinate systems is evidently not possible in the affine space nor in the Euclidean space due to the presence of the arbitrary constant ρ in the transformations (12.3) of the Euclidean group.

Now select a particular rectangular coordinate system in the Euclidean metric space and let y^i denote the coordinates of this system. Let us then transform the coordinates y^i by an arbitrary linear transformation

$$y^i = b_j^i x^j + c^i; \qquad |b_j^i| \neq 0, \tag{13.2}$$

where the b^i_j and c^i are constants subject only to the condition that the determinant $|b^i_j|$ does not vanish. The transformations (13.2) define a class of coordinate systems for the space which will be called *cartesian coordinate systems* and which will include, in particular, the preferred or rectangular coordinate systems. Between any two such cartesian systems, e.g. the x coordinate system defined by (13.2) and an $\bar{x}$ coordinate system defined in a similar manner, a transformation of the form (12.1) will hold. Thus the generality of the transformations between these cartesian systems is the same as that of the transformations between the cartesian coordinate systems of an affine space. But this does not mean that we have now passed from the Euclidean metric space to an affine space. For in the latter space the cartesian coordinate systems are preferred while in the Euclidean metric space only a subset of the cartesian systems, namely the rectangular coordinate systems, has the preferred status. However the introduction of the larger class of cartesian coordinate systems in the Euclidean metric space will be useful on occasion and will, moreover, enable us to carry over, without modification, certain of the formal relations in the theory of the Riemann space (see Sect. 6) to the case of the Euclidean metric space.

We shall now derive an expression which will give the distance between two points of a Euclidean metric space in terms of their cartesian coordinates. For this purpose suppose that the two points P_1 and P_2 have the coordinates y^i_1 and y^i_2 in a rectangular coordinate system and let x^i_1 and x^i_2 be the coordinates of these points in any one of the cartesian systems which is related to this rectangular system by a transformation of the form (13.2). Then the square of the distance between the points P_1 and P_2 is given by

$$(y^i_1 - y^i_2)(y^i_1 - y^i_2) = b^i_j(x^j_1 - x^j_2)\, b^i_k(x^k_1 - x^k_2) = g_{jk}(x^j_1 - x^j_2)(x^k_1 - x^k_2),$$

where we have put

$$g_{jk} = b^i_j\, b^i_k. \tag{13.3}$$

We associate the symmetric set of constants g_{jk} defined by (13.3) with the x coordinate system involved in the transformation (13.2). Now it can readily be seen that if we replace the particular rectangular coordinate system y used in the above determination of the constants g_{jk} by any other rectangular coordinate system the above association between sets of constants g_{jk} and cartesian coordinate systems will be unaltered. In other words the constants g_{jk} have a unique determination in each of the cartesian coordinate systems in the Euclidean metric space. Hence we can say without ambiguity that the square of the distance between two points is given by the expression

$$g_{jk}(x_1^j - x_2^j)(x_1^k - x_2^k), \tag{13.4}$$

where x_1^i and x_2^i are the coordinates of the points in a cartesian coordinate system and the g_{jk} are the above constants associated with this system.

To show that the g_{jk} are the components of a tensor under the affine group of transformations relating the cartesian coordinate systems we consider the equation

$$g_{jk}(x_1^j - x_2^j)(x_1^k - x_2^k) = \bar{g}_{pq}(\bar{x}_1^p - \bar{x}_2^p)(\bar{x}_1^q - \bar{x}_2^q), \tag{13.5}$$

the members of which give the square of the distance between the points P_1 and P_2 relative to any two cartesian coordinate systems. Since the coordinates x^i are related to the coordinates $\bar{x}^i$ by equations of the form (12.1) we can eliminate the $\bar{x}_1^i$ and $\bar{x}_2^i$ from (13.5) and thus obtain

$$[g_{jk} - \bar{g}_{pq}\, a_j^p\, a_k^q]\,(x_1^j - x_2^j)(x_1^k - x_2^k) = 0. \tag{13.6}$$

The tensor character of the g_{jk} under the affine group of transformations then follows from the fact that the bracket expressions in (13.6) must vanish since the values of the quantities $(x_1^i - x_2^i)$ are arbitrary.

We have now established the following result. *There exists a symmetric covariant tensor G whose components g_{jk} are constants in* *the cartesian coordinate systems and have the special values* δ_{jk} *in the preferred or rectangular coordinate systems of a Euclidean metric space; moreover the square of the distance between any two points* P_1 *and* P_2 *of the Euclidean metric space is given by the expression* (13.4) *in which* x_1^j *and* x_2^j *are the coordinates of the points in any one of the cartesian coordinate systems and the* g_{jk} *are the components of the tensor* G *relative to this system.*

It can readily be observed from the equations (13.3) that a quadratic form, having the components g_{jk} as its coefficients, is *positive definite.* Hence the determinant $|g_{jk}|$ must be positive and we can therefore define the components g^{jk} of a symmetric contravariant tensor, which can be though of as the contravariant form of the tensor G, by the equations (6.7) as shown in Sect. 6. By means of the tensor G the indices in the symbol for the components of a tensor can now be raised or lowered, one can define the length of a vector and the angle determined by two directions, etc. exactly as in Sect. 6. Thus the tensor G plays a role analogous to that of the fundamental metric tensor of a Riemann space.

Remark 1. One can adopt the viewpoint that a Riemann space *reduces* to a Euclidean metric space if there exists an allowable coordinate system $P \leftrightarrow (x^1,\ldots,x^n)$ in the Riemann space such that (a) the system $P \leftrightarrow (x^1,\ldots,x^n)$ is a (1,1) correspondence between the points P of the Riemann space and the points $(x^1,\ldots,x^n)$ of the arithmetic space of n dimensions and (b) relative to the system $P \leftrightarrow (x^1,\ldots,x^n)$ the components g_{ij} of the fundamental metric tensor of the Riemann space have the values δ_{ij}; this implies in particular that the Riemann space is topologically equivalent to the arithmetic space of n dimensions. Such a coordinate system $P \leftrightarrow (x^1,\ldots,x^n)$ may be called *preferred* and from these preferred systems one can pass to the cartesian coordinate systems as we have done in the above discussion of the Euclidean metric space.

A Riemann space is said to be *locally flat* if an arbitrary point of the space is contained in some allowable coordinate system relative to which the values δ_{ij} are assumed by the components of the fundamental metric tensor. The well known condition for a Riemann space to be locally flat is the vanishing of its curvature tensor (defined in Remark 1 in Sect. 11). A discussion of these and other results on the reducibility of spaces can be found in certain of the references listed at the end of this book.

Two geometrical entities of special interest and importance in the theory of the Euclidean metric space are the *straight line* and the *plane* which are defined by equations of the form

$$x^i = a^i t + b^i, \qquad (\textit{equations of straight line}), \tag{13.7}$$

$$A_i x^i + B = 0, \qquad (\textit{equation of plane}), \tag{13.8}$$

relative to any cartesian coordinate system. In the equations (13.7), which involve t as a parameter, the a^i are constants subject only to the condition that they do not all vanish while the b^i are completely arbitrary constants; likewise in (13.8) the A_i and B are constants subject only to the condition that not all of the A's are equal to zero. It is easily seen from the requirement that the equations (13.7) be invariant in form under affine transformations of the cartesian coordinate systems that the quantities $x^i - b^i$ and hence the coefficients a^i are the components of contravariant vectors. Similarly the coefficients A_i in the equation of the plane (13.8) can be interpreted as the components of a covariant vector A under affine transformations. Also it is easily seen that the vector A is perpendicular to the plane (13.8). In fact if P_1 and P_2 are two arbitrary distinct points in the plane (13.8) and if x_1^i and x_2^i are the coordinates of these points, then from (13.8) we have

$$A_i(x_1^i - x_2^i) = 0. \tag{13.9}$$

But the coordinate differences $x_1^i - x^i$ can evidently represent the components of an arbitrary contravariant vector in the plane (13.8). The condition (13.9) can therefore be interpreted as expressing the fact that the vector A is perpendicular to every vector in the plane (13.8) and hence, by definition, A is perpendicular to the plane.

One can give a formal presentation, based on the equations (13.7) and (13.8), of the direction cosines of a straight line or the determination of the angle between a straight line and a plane, etc.; in particular by considering the angles between the coordinate axes, defined in an obvious manner by means of the equations (13.7), it will follow that the axes of any preferred coordinate system are mutually orthogonal, a fact which justifies the designation of the preferred systems of the Euclidean metric space as *rectangular* coordinate systems. However we shall forego this discussion since these matters are treated adequately in books on elementary analytic geometry and instead we shall consider in the following Remarks several geometrical problems whose solution depends essentially on the concept of invariance under affine transformations.

Remark 2. Let A and B be two contravariant vectors at a point P of a Euclidean metric space of three dimensions. These vectors determine a parallelogram and we shall now treat the problem of finding its area. Precisely we seek an expression giving the area in terms of the conponents of the vectors A and B in any system of cartesian coordinates. We begin by choosing a rectangular coordinate system such that the origin is at the point P, the vector A falls along the positive x^1 axis and the vector B lies in the x^1,x^2 plane (Fig. 2). Relative to this coordinate system the area of the parallelogram is equal to the product $\pm A^1B^2$ where the $+$ sign is to be taken if B^2 is positive (as in Fig. 2), otherwise the $-$ sign.

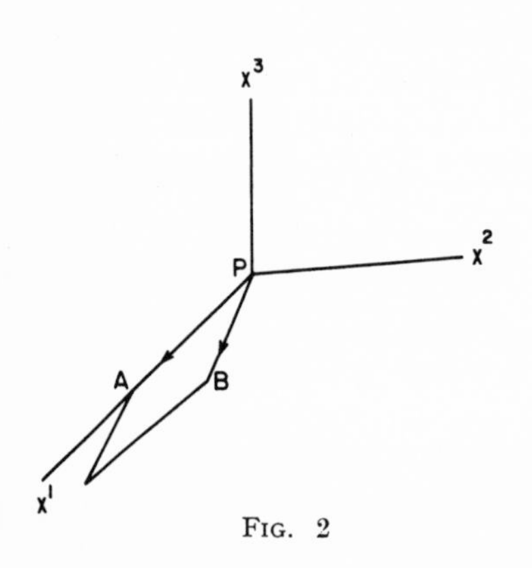

FIG. 2

Now under affine transformations (12.1) the quantities C_i defined by (6.5) transform by the equations $C_i = \pm \bar{C}_k a_i^k$ where the $+$ sign is chosen if (12.1) is a proper transformation otherwise the $-$ sign. Hence $g^{ij} C_i C_j$ defines a scalar function S under arbitrary affine transformations (12.1). But in the above rectangular coordinate system the tensor components g^{ij} are equal to the corresponding Kronecker δ^{ij} and the C_i have the values $C_1 = C_2 = 0$ and $C_3 = A^1B^2$. Hence the scalar S is equal to the square of the area of the parallelogram. Replacing the C_i in the expression for S by the values given by (6.5) we find that the desired expression for the area of the parallelogram is given by

$$(\text{Area})^2 = \varepsilon_{ijk}\, \varepsilon_{mrs}\, g^{im}\, A^j\, A^r\, B^k\, B^s.$$

If we denote by $\hat{A}$ and $\hat{B}$ the magnitudes of the vectors A and B respectively and make use of the second set of identities (6.16) we find that the above equation gives the usual formula

$$\text{Area} = \hat{A}\hat{B}\cos\theta,$$

for the area of the parallelogram where θ is the angle determined by the vectors A and B.

Remark 3. Consider the absolute scalar

$$(\varepsilon_{ijk}\, U^i\, V^j\, W^k)^2,$$

determined by three contravariant vectors U, V and W at a point P in a Euclidean metric space of three dimensions. What is the geometrical meaning of this scalar? To answer this question we attempt to clarify the problem by a judicious choice of coordinate system. Thus let us select a rectangular coordinate system with origin at P such that the vector U falls along the positive x^1 axis and the vector V lies in the x^1,x^2 plane (Fig. 3). Relative to this coordinate system we see that

$$\varepsilon_{ijk}\, U^i\, V^j\, W^k = U^1\, V^2\, W^3.$$

Now to within algebraic sign U^1V^2 is twice the area of the triangle determined by the vectors U and V and hence, also to within algebraic sign, $U^1V^2W^3$ is six times the volume of the tetrehedron determined by the three vectors U, V and W. Hence in any system of cartesian coordinates we have

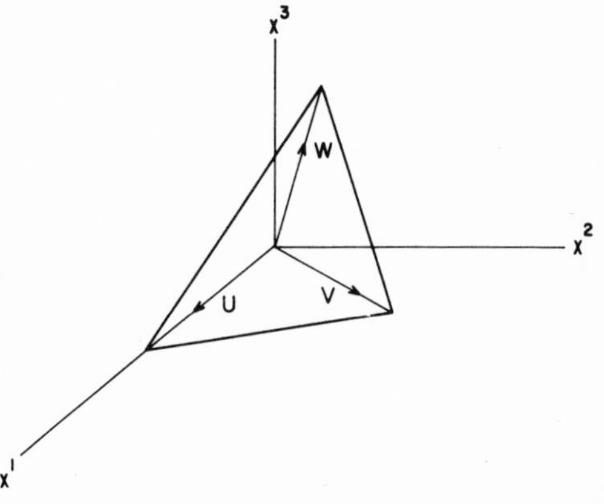

FIG. 3

$$36\,(\text{Volume})^2 = (\varepsilon_{ijk}\, U^i\, V^j\, W^k)^2.$$

This equation likewise gives the volume of the tetrehedron determined by four arbitrary points P, Q, R and S since we can take

$$U^i = x^i_2 - x^i_1; \qquad V^i = x^i_3 - x^i_1; \qquad W^i = x^i_4 - x^i_1,$$

where x^i_1, x^i_2, x^i_3 and x^i_4 are the coordinates of P, Q, R and S respectively in any cartesian coordinate system.

Remark 4. Let us now consider the problem of finding the perpendicular distance from an arbitrary point P in a three dimensional Euclidean metric space to a given plane (13.8) in this space. To determine this distance we choose a system of rectangular coordinates y^i such that (a) the y^1,y^2 coordinate plane coincides with the plane (13.8) and (b) the point P lies on the positive y^3 axis (Fig. 4). Hence if $\overset{i}{y_0}$ are the coordinates of P in this rectangular system the coordinate $\overset{3}{y_0}$ will be equal to the required distance. Our problem is now reduced to the construction of a scalar function of the coordinates of P which is equal, to within algebraic sign, to the coordinate $\overset{3}{y_0}$ in the above rectangular system. But such a scalar is readily seen to be given by

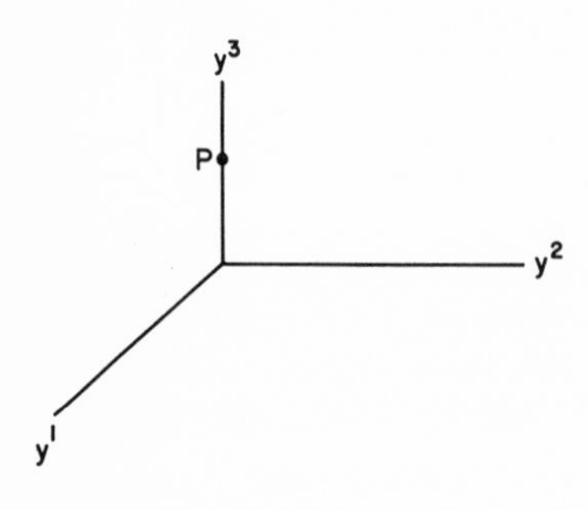

FIG. 4

$$\frac{a_i \overset{i}{x_0} + b^i}{\sqrt{g^{ij} a_i a_j}},$$

where the $\overset{i}{x_0}$ are the coordinates of P in the cartesian coordinate system relative to which the equation (13.8) determines the plane under consideration.

Remark 5. It is evident from the above discussion that invariance under coordinate transformations is a common property of the equations which define geometrical configurations and the magnitudes associated with them. If, however, we wish to express this fact as a principle of the Euclidean metric geometry it is well to bear in mind that the basic structure of the Euclidean metric space is determined by the class of preferred or rectangular coordinate systems rather than the larger class of cartesian systems and that all rectangular coordinate systems appear on an equal footing in our conception of the Euclidean metric space. With these ideas before us we can make the following statement concerning the province of the Euclidean metric geometry. *Euclidean metric geometry, as treated analytically by means of rectangular coordinate systems, is the study of those configurations and their associated magnitudes which remain invariant under the group of orthogonal transformations.* A similar principle can of course be stated for the affine and strict Euclidean geometries as well as for those other geometries which arise from various choices of the group G in the axiomatic characterization of the class of spaces discussed in Sect. 12.

14. Homogeneous and Isotropic Tensors

Roughly speaking a material medium, e.g. a fluid or a solid, is said to be *homogeneous* if its properties are independent of position and *isotropic* if they are independent of direction. These properties have their precise mathematical expression in the so-called homogeneous and isotropic tensors. By a *homogeneous tensor* in a Euclidean metric space is understood a tensor whose components are constants in any one of the preferred or rectangular coordinate systems commonly used as reference frames for the medium. An *isotropic tensor* in the Euclidean metric space is defined as a tensor such that its components, in any rectangular system, are unaltered in value by orthogonal transformations of coordinates. The homogeneous tensor poses no mathematical problem since the required condition, i.e. the condition of homogeneity, can be satisfied by the direct assumption that the components of the tensor are constant in any rectangular system. Hence we need concern ourselves only with the problem of the isotropic tensor. In discussing this problem we shall limit our attention (α) to a space of three dimensions and (β) to a fourth order tensor C, whose components C^{ij}_{km} are symmetric in the two contravariant and also in the two covariant indices, since one is commonly concerned with a tensor of this type in the mechanics of a continuous medium. The method employed, however, can be applied to tensors of any order and several simple illustrations are given in the Remark at the end of this section.

We may express the components of the above tensor C in the completely covariant form C_{ijkm} since there is no distinction between covariant and contravariant indices relative to a rectangular coordinate system. Now consider a one parameter family of proper orthogonal rotations (12.2), e.g. transformations (12.2) with $b^i = 0$, such that (1) the coefficients a^i_j are continuous and differentiable functions of a parameter t for $0 \leqslant t \leqslant t_0$ and (2) the condition $a^i_j = \delta^i_j$ for $t = 0$ is satisfied, i.e. the rotation (12.2) is the identity transformation for the initial value of the parameter. Under any transformation of this family the components C_{ijkm} will transform by the equations

$$C_{ijkm} = C_{pqrs}\, a^p_i(t)\, a^q_j(t)\, a^r_k(t)\, a^s_m(t), \tag{14.1}$$

in which account is taken of the isotropic character of the tensor C, i.e. the invariance of the values of the components C_{ijkm}. Now differentiate (14.1) with respect to t and then evaluate the resulting relations at $t = 0$. Since the quantities C_{ijkm} are independent of t we thus obtain

$$C_{ajkm}\,\omega_{ai} + C_{iakm}\,\omega_{aj} + C_{ijam}\,\omega_{ak} + C_{ijka}\,\omega_{am} = 0, \tag{14.2}$$

where ω_{ij} stands for the derivative of $a^i_j(t)$ at $t = 0$. But if we differentiate the second set of relations (12.2) with respect to t and then evaluate at $t = 0$ we find that $\omega_{ij} + \omega_{ji} = 0$, i.e. the quantities ω_{ij} are skew-symmetric. Obviously the condition of skew-symmetry is the only restriction on the quantities ω. Hence there are exactly three independent quantities ω_{ij} and it is therefore possible to express them by writing

$$\omega_{ij} = e_{ijk}\,\xi^k, \tag{14.3}$$

where the e_{ijk} are the components of the skew-symmetric tensor defined in Sect. 4 and the ξ^k are three arbitrary variables. Eliminating the ω_{ij} from (14.2) by means of (14.3) the coefficients of the independent variables ξ^k in the resulting equations must be equal to zero. We thus find that the C_{ijkm} must satisfy the following conditions

$$C_{ajkm}\,e_{iab} + C_{iakm}\,e_{jab} + C_{ijam}\,e_{kab} + C_{ijka}\,e_{mab} = 0. \tag{14.4}$$

Let us now multiply (14.4) by e^{ibc} and sum on the repeated indices i and b; but this leads to the equations

$$3\,C_{ijkm} + C_{ikmj} + C_{imjk} = C_{aakm}\,\delta_{ij} + C_{iaam}\,\delta_{jk} + C_{iaak}\,\delta_{jm}, \tag{14.5}$$

after application of the relations (4.7) and some relabeling of the free indices. To obtain more explicit information regarding the structure of the components C_{ijkm} than is furnished by the above conditions let us first observe that (14.5) can be written in the following three equivalent forms

$$\left.\begin{aligned} &2\,C_{ijkm} + (C_{ijkm} + C_{ikmj} + C_{imjk}) \\ &= C_{akm}\delta_{ij} + C_{iaam}\,\delta_{jk} + C_{iaak}\,\delta_{jm}, \end{aligned}\right\} \tag{14.6}$$

$$\left.\begin{aligned} &2\,C_{ikmj} + (C_{ikmj} + C_{imjk} + C_{ijkm}) \\ &= C_{aamj}\,\delta_{ik} + C_{iaaj}\,\delta_{km} + C_{iaam}\,\delta_{jk}, \end{aligned}\right\} \tag{14.7}$$

$$\left.\begin{aligned} &2\,C_{imjk} + (C_{imjk} + C_{ijkm} + C_{ikmj}) \\ &= C_{aajk}\,\delta_{im} + C_{iaak}\,\delta_{mj} + C_{iaaj}\,\delta_{mk}. \end{aligned}\right\} \tag{14.8}$$

Actually the equations (14.6) are identical with (14.5) except for a slight rearrangement of terms in the left members while the equations (14.7) and (14.8) are obtained from (14.6) by cyclic permutation of the indices j,k,m. Adding corresponding members of these equations we now have

$$\left.\begin{aligned} 5\,(C_{ijkm} + C_{ikmj} + C_{imjk}) &= 2\,(C_{iaaj}\,\delta_{km} + C_{iaak}\,\delta_{jm} + C_{iaam}\,\delta_{jk}) \\ &\quad + C_{aakm}\,\delta_{ij} + C_{aajm}\,\delta_{ik} + C_{aajk}\,\delta_{im}. \end{aligned}\right\} \tag{14.9}$$

Then, using (14.9) to eliminate the parenthesis expression in (14.6), we find that

$$\left.\begin{aligned} 10\,C_{ijkm} &= 4\,C_{aakm}\,\delta_{ij} - C_{aamj}\,\delta_{ik} - C_{aajk}\delta_{im} + 3\,C_{iaam}\,\delta_{jk} \\ &\quad + 3\,C_{iaak}\,\delta_{jm} - 2\,C_{iaaj}\,\delta_{km}. \end{aligned}\right\} \tag{14.10}$$

It remains to express the partially contracted components of the tensor C which appear in the right members of (14.10) by expressions in the completely contracted components of this tensor. For this purpose let us put $k = m$ and $j = k$ in turn in the equations (14.5) and in each case sum on the repeated indices. We thus obtain the following two sets of relations

$$C_{aaij} = C_{ijaa} = \tfrac{1}{3}\,C_{aabb}\,\delta_{ij}. \tag{14.11}$$

Again, putting $i = m$ in (14.5) and summing on the repeated indices, we are led to the equations

$$2\,C_{jaak} = C_{baab}\,\delta_{jk} - C_{kaaj}, \tag{14.12}$$

or

$$2\,C_{kaaj} = C_{baab}\,\delta_{jk} - C_{jaak}, \tag{14.13}$$

when we interchange the indices j and k. But combining (14.12) and (14.13) we find immediately that $C_{jaak} = C_{kaaj}$. Hence (14.12) yields

$$C_{jaak} = \tfrac{1}{3}\,C_{baab}\,\delta_{jk}. \tag{14.14}$$

Making the substitutions (14.11) and (14.14) in the right members of (14.10) these equations can now be written in the form

$$C_{ijkm} = \lambda\,\delta_{ij}\,\delta_{km} + \mu(\delta_{ik}\,\delta_{jm} + \delta_{im}\,\delta_{jk}), \tag{14.15}$$

where

$$\left.\begin{aligned} \lambda &= \frac{2}{15}\,C_{aabb} - \frac{1}{15}\,C_{baab}, \\ \mu &= \frac{1}{10}\,C_{baab} - \frac{1}{30}\,C_{aabb}. \end{aligned}\right\}$$

From the above equations for λ and μ we see that these quantities are scalars. But conversely a tensor C having components C_{ijkm} given by (14.15) in which λ and μ are scalars is an isotropic tensor. Hence we can state the following result. *If the components C^{ij}_{km} of an isotropic tensor C are symmetric in the indices i,j and also in the indices k,m then*

$$C^{ij}_{km} = \lambda\delta^{ij}\,\delta_{km} + \mu(\delta^i_k\,\delta^j_m + \delta^i_m\,\delta^j_k), \tag{14.16}$$

in a rectangular system, where the quantities λ and μ are scalar functions of the coordinates.

It is immediately seen that if the tensor C is both homogeneous and isotropic the scalars λ and μ must be constants. In fact putting $i = k$, $j = m$ and also $i = j$, $k = m$ in (14.16) and summing on repeated indices we obtain

$$\lambda + 4\,\mu = \text{const.}; \qquad 3\,\lambda + 2\,\mu = \text{const.},$$

since the C's are constant by hypothesis. But from these equations it follows that λ and μ are constants as stated.

Remark. Consider the possibility of an isotropic vector V. For such a vector we have

$$V_i = V_p\, a_i^p\,(t); \qquad V_a\, \omega_{ai} = 0; \qquad V_a\, e_{aib} = 0, \tag{14.17}$$

corresponding to the equations (14.1), (14.2) and (14.4) respectively. Multiplying the last set of equations (14.17) by e^{cjb} and summing on the repeated index b we obtain

$$V_a\, e_{aib}\, e^{cjb} = V_a(\delta_{ac}\,\delta_{ij} - \delta_{aj}\,\delta_{ic}) = V_c\,\delta_{ij} - V_j\,\delta_{ic} = 0. \tag{14.18}$$

But if we put $i = j$ in (14.18) and sum on the repeated index we find that $V_i = 0$. *Hence there is no non-vanishing isotropic vector.*

As another illustration of the use of the above method let us seek to determine the structure of an isotropic tensor W of the second order. Then in place of (14.1), (14.2) and (14.4) we have

$$\left.\begin{aligned} W_{ij} = W_{pq}\, a_i^p\, a_j^q; \qquad W_{aj}\,\omega_{ai} + W_{ia}\,\omega_{aj} = 0; \\ W_{aj}\, e_{aik} + W_{ia}\, e_{ajk} = 0, \end{aligned}\right\} \tag{14.19}$$

respectively. Multiplying the third set of equations (14.19) by e^{bmk} and summing on the repeated index k we are led to conditions of the form

$$W_{ij}\,\delta_{km} - W_{mj}\,\delta_{ik} + W_{ki}\,\delta_{jm} - W_{km}\,\delta_{ij} = 0. \tag{14.20}$$

Putting $k = m$ in (14.20) and summing on the repeated index we obtain

$$2\,W_{ij} + W_{ji} = W_{aa}\,\delta_{ij}, \tag{14.21}$$

or

$$2\,W_{ji} + W_{ij} = W_{aa}\,\delta_{ij}. \tag{14.22}$$

But, combining (14.21) and (14.22), it follows that $W_{ij} = W_{ji}$ and hence (14.21) reduces to

$$W_{ij} = \lambda\,\delta_{ij}; \qquad \lambda = \tfrac{1}{3}\,W_{aa}. \tag{14.23}$$

Hence any isotropic tensor W of the second order will have components W_{ij} given, in a rectangular coordinate system, by (14.23) *in which λ is a scalar.*

15. Curves in Space. Frenet Formulae

Let R be an oriented Riemann space of three dimensions and C a regular curve in R (see Sect. 6). We assume that C is defined parametrically by functions $x^i(s)$ where the x^i are the coordinates of an allowable system in R and s denotes arc length along C. By differentiation of the equations which represent any allowable coordinate transformation $x \leftrightarrow \bar{x}$ in R it readily follows that the quantities

$$\lambda^i(s) = \frac{dx^i(s)}{ds}, \tag{15.1}$$

which are defined along C as functions of the arc length s, are the components of a contravariant vector λ. Moreover it is immediately seen that λ is a unit vector, i.e.

$$g_{ij}\,\lambda^i\,\lambda^j = 1. \tag{15.2}$$

The vector λ is said to be *tangent* to the curve C.

By absolute differentiation with respect to the parameter s (see Sect. 10) it follows from (15.2) that

$$g_{ij}\,\lambda^i \frac{D\lambda^j}{Ds} = 0. \tag{15.3}$$

A vector perpendicular to the tangent vector λ is said to be *normal* to the curve C; hence it follows from (15.3) that the absolute derivative of λ is normal to C. Now define a positive function κ of s by writing

$$\kappa = \sqrt{g_{ij}\frac{D\lambda^i}{Ds}\frac{D\lambda^j}{Ds}}\,. \tag{15.4}$$

Then the vector ξ having the components

$$\xi^i = \frac{1}{\kappa} \frac{D\lambda^i}{Ds}, \tag{15.5}$$

is a unit vector normal to C, i.e.

$$g_{ij}\, \xi^i\, \xi^j = 1; \qquad g_{ij}\, \lambda^i\, \xi^j = 0. \tag{15.6}$$

The vector ξ is called the *principal normal* and the scalar function κ is called the *curvature* of the curve C.

Since ξ is a unit vector we have

$$g_{ij}\, \xi^i \frac{D\xi^j}{Ds} = 0, \tag{15.7}$$

corresponding to (15.3). Also by absolute differentiation of the second set of relations (15.6) we find that

$$g_{ij}\, \lambda^i \frac{D\xi^j}{Ds} = -\, g_{ij} \frac{D\lambda^i}{Ds}\, \xi^j = -\, \kappa\, g_{ij}\, \xi^i\, \xi^j = -\, \kappa, \tag{15.8}$$

when use is made of (15.5) and the fact that ξ is a unit vector. In addition we observe that

$$g_{ij}\, \lambda^i \left(\frac{D\xi^j}{Ds} + \kappa\, \lambda^j \right) = 0; \qquad g_{ij}\, \xi^i \left(\frac{D\xi^j}{Ds} + \kappa\, \lambda^j \right) = 0. \tag{15.9}$$

The first of these relations is obtained from (15.2) and (15.8) while the second set of the relations follows from (15.7) and the second condition (15.6). Hence the quantities in parenthesis in (15.9) are the components of a vector which is perpendicular to λ and ξ. Corresponding to the above procedure we now define a unit vector ζ, perpendicular to λ and ξ, by writing

$$\zeta^i = \frac{1}{\tau} \left(\frac{D\xi^i}{Ds} + \kappa\, \lambda^i \right). \tag{15.10}$$

The above quantity τ and hence the components ζ^i defined by (15.10) are determined to within algebraic sign by the requirement that ζ is a unit vector. To remove this ambiguity regarding algebraic sign we postulate that the vector triad λ,ξ,ζ has a *positive orientation*, i.e. that at any point P of the curve C we can find an allowable coordinate system S with origin at P such that, if the coordinates of S are denoted by y^i, the vectors λ,ξ,ζ have the directions of the positive y^1,y^2,y^3 axes respectively. Relative to the system S it is seen immediately that $g_{ij} = \delta_{ij}$ at the point P and also that

$$\varepsilon_{ijk}\,\lambda^i\,\xi^j\,\zeta^k = 1, \tag{15.11}$$

where the ε_{ijk} are the components of the skew-symmetric tensor ε defined in Sect. 6. Hence (15.11) must be satisfied along C in any allowable system because of the invariant nature of this relation. Conversely it is readily observed that the condition (15.11) implies the positive orientation of the vector triad λ,ξ,ζ and hence (15.11) can be taken as the condition for the determination of the algebraic sign of the components ζ^i or of the scalar quantity τ; as so determined τ may be positive or negative. The unit vector ζ, defined uniquely by (15.10) and (15.11), is called the *binormal* and the associated scalar τ the *torsion* of the curve C.

Using the fact that the components g_{ij} have the values δ_{ij} at the origin of the above y coordinate system we observe that the relations

$$\left.\begin{array}{c} \zeta^k = \varepsilon_{ijm}\,g^{mk}\,\lambda^i\,\xi^j; \qquad \xi^k = -\,\varepsilon_{ijm}\,g^{mk}\,\lambda^i\,\zeta^j; \\ \lambda^k = \varepsilon_{ijm}\,g^{mk}\,\xi^i\,\zeta^j \end{array}\right\} \tag{15.12}$$

are satisfied at the origin of this system and hence they are satisfied along the curve C in any allowable coordinate system. Each of the above three sets of relations (15.12) is obviously equivalent to the condition (15.11). Let us now take the absolute derivative of the two members of the first set of relations (15.12) to obtain

$$\frac{D\zeta^k}{Ds} = \varepsilon_{ijm}\,g^{mk}\,\frac{D\lambda^i}{Ds}\,\xi^j + \varepsilon_{ijm}\,g^{mk}\,\lambda^i\,\frac{D\xi^j}{Ds}\,.$$

Then, eliminating the derivatives $D\lambda^i/Ds$ and $D\xi^i/Ds$ by the substitutions (15.5) and (15.10) the above equations are seen to reduce to

$$\frac{D\zeta^k}{Ds} = \tau\, \varepsilon_{ijm}\, g^{mk}\, \lambda^i\, \zeta^j = -\tau\, \xi^k, \tag{15.13}$$

when use is made of the second set of equations (15.12). Combining (15.13) with the equations (15.5) and (15.10) we obtain the *Frenet formulae* for the curve C, namely

$$\left.\begin{aligned} \frac{D\lambda^i}{Ds} &= \kappa\, \xi^i, \\ \frac{D\xi^i}{Ds} &= \tau\, \zeta^i - \kappa\, \lambda^i, \\ \frac{D\zeta^i}{Ds} &= -\tau\, \xi^i. \end{aligned}\right\} \tag{15.14}$$

Remark 1. An explicit formula for the torsion τ is given by

$$\tau = \varepsilon_{ijk}\, \lambda^i\, \xi^j \frac{D\xi^k}{Ds}\,. \tag{15.15}$$

To verify the equation (15.15) we have merely to eliminate the derivatives $D\xi^k/Ds$ in the right member by means of (15.10); the resulting equation is then seen to be satisfied identically in view of the skew-symmetry of the components ε_{ijk} and the condition (15.11).

Remark 2. In the special case for which the Riemann space R is a Euclidean metric space E of three dimensions, referred to its preferred or rectangular coordinate systems, there is no distinction between absolute and ordinary differentiation in the Frenet formulae (15.14) and hence these formulae reduce to

$$\frac{d\lambda^i}{ds} = \kappa\xi^i; \qquad \frac{d\xi^i}{ds} = \tau\zeta^i - \kappa\lambda^i; \qquad \frac{d\zeta^i}{ds} = -\tau\xi^i. \tag{15.16}$$

Now suppose that the curve C under consideration is a *plane curve* in the above Euclidean metric space E, i.e. the curve C lies in a plane (13.8). Then we must have

$$A_i\lambda^i = 0; \qquad A_i\xi^i = 0. \tag{15.17}$$

In fact the first equation (15.17) follows if we differentiate (13.8) with respect to the arc length s and then make the substitution (15.1); similarly we obtain the second equation (15.17) by differentiation of the first equation and use of the first equation (15.16) under the assumption that the curvature κ is different from zero. But the quantities A_i are the components of a vector A perpendicular to the plane (13.8) as observed in Sect. 13; also this vector A must be perpendicular to the vectors λ and ξ on account of (15.17). Hence the vectors λ, ξ, A form a set of three mutually perpendicular vectors at points of the curve C. But the vectors λ, ξ, ζ also form a mutually perpendicular set of vectors along C and hence, since there is no distinction between covariant and contravariant indices relative to rectangular coordinate systems, it is clear that $A_i \sim \zeta^i$, i.e. the components of the vectors A and ζ are proportional. Hence ζ is perpendicular to the plane containing the curve C and, since ζ is a unit vector, it follows that its components ζ^i must be constant along C. Hence from the last equation (15.16) we see that $\tau = 0$, i.e. the above assumption $\tau \neq 0$ is untenable. *The torsion of a plane curve is therefore equal to zero, and hence, for a plane curve, the Frenet formulae* (15.16) *reduce to*

$$\frac{d\lambda^i}{ds} = \kappa\xi^i; \qquad \frac{d\xi^i}{ds} = -\kappa\lambda^i. \tag{15.18}$$

If we do not restrict ourselves to the use of rectangular or cartesian coordinate systems in the space E we must obviously replace the ordinary derivatives by absolute derivatives in the relations (15.18), i.e. we must take

$$\frac{D\lambda^i}{Ds} = \kappa\xi^i; \qquad \frac{D\xi^i}{Ds} = -\kappa\lambda^i, \tag{15.19}$$

to secure the proper form of the Frenet formulae for the plane curve C.

16. Surfaces in Space

A set of points S in a three dimensional Riemann space R will be said to be a *regular surface* if, neighboring an arbitrary point P of S, the points can be represented by equations of the form

$$x^i = \phi^i(u^1, u^2), \tag{16.1}$$

where the x^i are the coordinates of any allowable system in R and the ϕ^i are differentiable functions of the two parameters u^1,u^2 such that the functional matrix

$$\left\| \begin{matrix} \dfrac{\partial \phi^1}{\partial u^1} & \dfrac{\partial \phi^2}{\partial u^1} & \dfrac{\partial \phi^3}{\partial u^1} \\ \\ \dfrac{\partial \phi^1}{\partial u^2} & \dfrac{\partial \phi^2}{\partial u^2} & \dfrac{\partial \phi^3}{\partial u^2} \end{matrix} \right\|$$

has rank 2. If the ϕ^i are of class C^r as functions of the parameters u^1,u^2 we may say that the surface S is of class C^r. One commonly refers to the parameters u^1,u^2 as the *curvilinear coordinates* of the surface. In the case of a regular surface S of class C^r the system of curvilinear coordinates u^1,u^2 will be said to be *allowable* and (1,1) transformations $u \leftrightarrow \bar{u}$ of class C^r of the coordinates of the system u will result in an allowable coordinate system $\bar{u}$ for the surface S.

Consider the quantities x^i_α defined by

$$x^i_\alpha = \frac{\partial x^i}{\partial u^\alpha}, \qquad (i = 1,2,3; \quad \alpha = 1,2). \tag{16.2}$$

Under allowable coordinate transformations $x \leftrightarrow \bar{x}$ these quantities are the components of two contravariant vectors in the space R and correspondingly under allowable coordinate transformations $u \leftrightarrow \bar{u}$ the quantities are the components of three covariant vectors on the surface S. Now any vector tangent to a curve on the surface S is said to be tangent to this surface. Hence the two space vectors having the components x^i_1 and x^i_2 are tangent to the surface S since these vectors, by definition, are tangent to the u^1 and u^2 coordinate curves respectively (see Sect. 15). Observe also that between the differentials du^α of the surface coordinates and the corresponding differentials dx^i of the space coordinates we have the relations

$$dx^i = x^i_\alpha \, du^\alpha, \qquad (i = 1,2,3; \quad \alpha = 1,2), \tag{16.3}$$

in which the quantities du^α and dx^i can be interpreted as the surface and space components of the same vector, e.g. a *displacement* on the surface S. More generally it is evident that a surface vector ξ having the components ξ^α will be related to the space components ξ^i of this vector by the equations

$$\xi^i = x^i_\alpha \, \xi^\alpha, \qquad (i = 1,2,3; \quad \alpha = 1,2), \tag{16.4}$$

and that any such vector ξ, considered as a vector in the space R, will be tangent to the surface S.

Let us now define a set of functions $g_{\alpha\beta}(u)$ of the coordinates u^1,u^2 of a regular surface S by writing

$$g_{\alpha\beta}(u) = g_{ij}(x) \frac{\partial x^i}{\partial u^\alpha} \frac{\partial x^j}{\partial u^\beta}, \tag{16.5}$$

where the indices α,β have the range 1,2 and the indices i,j the range 1,2,3. This convention regarding indices will be adopted in the following discussion, i.e. it will be assumed that Greek indices have the range 1,2 and Latin indices the range 1,2,3; within their respective ranges the summation convention, in accordance with which the repetition of an index in any term implies a summation on this index, will apply both to Greek and Latin indices. We have, moreover, used the Greek and Latin indices as an aid in distinguishing between the quantities $g_{\alpha\beta}$ defined on the surface S by the equations (16.5) and the components g_{ij} of the fundamental metric tensor of the Riemann space R.

It is immediately seen from (16.5) that the quantities $g_{\alpha\beta}$ transform by the equations

$$\bar{g}_{\mu\nu} = g_{\alpha\beta} \frac{\partial u^\alpha}{\partial \bar{u}^\mu} \frac{\partial u^\beta}{\partial \bar{u}^\nu}, \tag{16.6}$$

under allowable transformations $u \leftrightarrow \bar{u}$ of the curvilinear coordinates. Hence the $g_{\alpha\beta}$ are the components of a symmetric covariant tensor over the surface S; moreover the components $g_{\alpha\beta}$ of this tensor will be the coefficients of a *positive definite* quadratic differential form

$$ds^2 = g_{\alpha\beta}\, du^\alpha\, du^\beta. \tag{16.7}$$

In fact from (16.5) we have

$$g_{\alpha\beta}\, du^\alpha\, du^\beta = g_{ij} \left(\frac{\partial x^i}{\partial u^\alpha} du^\alpha \right) \left(\frac{\partial x^j}{\partial u^\beta} du^\beta \right). \tag{16.8}$$

Since the matrix $\|\partial x^i/\partial u^\alpha\|$ has rank 2 by hypothesis it follows that the parenthesis expressions in (16.8) can vanish if, and only if, the two differentials du^α are equal to zero. Hence we see from (16.8) and the fact that the g_{ij} are the coefficients of a positive definite quadratic form (6.1) that (a) the quadratic form (16.7) can vanish if, and only if, the du^α are zero and (b) the form (16.7) will otherwise be positive, i.e. the quadratic form (16.7) is positive definite as stated. The quadratic differential form (16.7) is called the *first fundamental form of the surface S*. The surface S, over which the element of distance ds is given by (16.7), is intrinsically a Riemann space of two dimensions having the coefficients $g_{\alpha\beta}$ of the quadratic form (16.7) as the components of its fundamental metric tensor. Determinations of the lengths of curves and vectors, the angle between two directions, etc. on the surface S, based on the metric of this surface, will be consistent with the corresponding space determinations in view of the relations (16.5) between the components of the metric tensors of the surface S and the space R.

A vector ξ will be said to be *normal* to a surface at a point P if it is perpendicular to every vector tangent to the surface at P.

Assume for the moment that the surface S is *oriented*, i.e. the allowable coordinate systems are related by transformations $u \leftrightarrow \bar{u}$ whose functional determinants are positive; consequently the quantities $\varepsilon_{\alpha\beta}$ defined in Remark 4, Sect. 6, will be the components of a skew-symmetric tensor of the second order. We now consider the problem of finding the components of a vector which will be normal to the oriented surface S. Observe first of all that the condition of normality will be satisfied if ξ is perpendicular to two *independent* tangent vectors at points P of the surface. Now the above tangent vectors having the components x^i_1 and x^i_2 are independent since the matrix $||x^i_\alpha||$ has rank 2 by hypothesis. Hence the condition that the vector ξ be normal to the surface S is given by

$$x^i_\alpha \, \xi_i = 0, \tag{16.9}$$

in terms of the covariant components ξ_i of ξ. By the well known theorem for the solution of a system of linear homogeneous equations (16.9) the components ξ_1, ξ_2 and ξ_3 are proportional to the following three determinants

$$\begin{vmatrix} x^2_1 & x^3_1 \\ x^2_2 & x^3_2 \end{vmatrix}; \quad \begin{vmatrix} x^3_1 & x^1_1 \\ x^3_2 & x^1_2 \end{vmatrix}; \quad \begin{vmatrix} x^1_1 & x^2_1 \\ x^1_2 & x^2_2 \end{vmatrix}. \tag{16.10}$$

To express the above result in invariant form we have merely to observe that the components of a vector ν defined by either of the following two sets of relations

$$\left.\begin{aligned} \nu_i &= \tfrac{1}{2}\, \varepsilon^{\alpha\beta}\, \varepsilon_{ijk}\, x^j_\alpha\, x^k_\beta, \\ \nu_i &= -\tfrac{1}{2}\, \varepsilon^{\alpha\beta}\, \varepsilon_{ijk}\, x^j_\alpha\, x^k_\beta, \end{aligned}\right\} \tag{16.11}$$

will be proportional to the quantities (16.10). Such a vector ν will therefore be normal to the surface S. Moreover by choosing coordinate systems such that $g_{\alpha\beta} = \delta_{\alpha\beta}$ and $g_{ij} = \delta_{ij}$ at a point P of the surface it can readily be seen that each of the vectors ν defined by (16.11) is a unit vector. *Hence the vectors* ν *given by* (16.11) *will be unit normal vectors to the oriented surface* S. In any specific problem one or the other of the vectors ν defined by (16.11) should be chosen according to the direction which one may wish to assign to the unit normal to the surface.

Remark 1. Since the matrix $||x_\alpha^i||$ has rank 2 it follows from the implicit function theorem that two of the three equations (16.1) can be solved for the variables u^1, u^2; the solution functions can then be used to eliminate the variables u^1, u^2 from the remaining equation (16.1). Hence the surface S can always be represented locally by an equation of the form

$$f(x^1, x^2, x^3) = 0, \tag{16.12}$$

where f is a continuous and differentiable function of the space coordinates. Eliminating the coordinates x^i from (16.12) by means of (16.1) the resulting equations must be satisfied identically in the independent variables u^1 and u^2; hence we must have

$$\frac{\partial f}{\partial x^i} x_\alpha^i = 0.$$

In other words the gradient of the function f is normal to the surface S. Corresponding to (16.11) we may now say that the components of the two unit vectors, normal to the surface S, are given by

$$\nu_i = \frac{\partial f / \partial x^i}{\sqrt{g^{jk} \dfrac{\partial f}{\partial x^j} \dfrac{\partial f}{\partial x^k}}}; \qquad \nu_i = \frac{-\partial f / \partial x^i}{\sqrt{g^{jk} \dfrac{\partial f}{\partial x^j} \dfrac{\partial f}{\partial x^k}}}.$$

Remark 2. Denoting the contravariant components of the unit normal by ν^i we have

$$g_{ij} x_\alpha^i \nu^j = 0, \tag{16.13}$$

as the condition for the vector ν to be normal to the surface S. We can now effect a formal combination of the equations (16.5) and (16.13) in the following manner. Put $x_3^i = \nu^i$ and define quantities G_{ij} by writing

$$G_{\alpha\beta} = g_{\alpha\beta}; \qquad G_{3\beta} = G_{\alpha 3} = 0; \qquad G_{33} = 1.$$

Then we shall have

$$g_{ij} x_k^i x_m^j = G_{km}. \tag{16.14}$$

In fact if $k = \alpha$, $m = \beta$ the relations (16.14) reduce to (16.5); if $k = 3$, $m = \beta$ or if $k = \alpha$, $m = 3$ the relations (16.14) are equivalent to (16.13); finally if $k = m = 3$ we see that (16.14) gives the condition for ν to be a unit vector.

From the above definition of the G_{ij} we observe that the determinants $|G_{ij}|$ and $|g_{\alpha\beta}|$ are equal in value. Hence $|G_{ij}|$ does not vanish. Taking the determinants of both members of (16.14) we see that the determinant $|x^i_j|$ must likewise be different from zero. Hence we can define quantities y^i_j and symmetric quantities G^{ij} such that

$$x^i_k \, y^k_j = \delta^i_j; \qquad G_{ij} G^{ik} = \delta^k_j. \tag{16.15}$$

Using the relations (16.15) we can now deduce the following modifications of the equations (16.14) by performing the indicated operations, namely

$$g_{ia} \, x^i_k = G_{km} \, y^m_a, \quad \text{multiplying (16.14) by } y^m_a, \tag{16.16}$$

$$x^b_k = G_{km} \, g^{ab} \, y^m_a, \quad \text{multiplying (16.16) by } g^{ab}, \tag{16.17}$$

$$G^{ik} \, x^b_k = g^{ab} \, y^i_a, \quad \text{multiplying (16.17) by } G^{ik}. \tag{16.18}$$

Finally multiplying (16.18) by x^c_i we obtain a set of relations which can be written

$$g^{ij} = G^{km} \, x^i_k \, x^j_m. \tag{16.19}$$

Expanding the right members of (16.19) these relations become

$$g^{ij} = G^{\alpha\beta} \, x^i_\alpha \, x^j_\beta + G^{3\beta} \, x^i_3 \, x^j_\beta + G^{\alpha 3} \, x^i_\alpha \, x^j_3 + G^{33} \, x^i_3 \, x^j_3. \tag{16.20}$$

But from the above conditions (16.15) defining the G^{ij} we have

$$G^{\alpha\beta} = g^{\alpha\beta}; \qquad G^{3\beta} = G^{\alpha 3} = 0; \qquad G^{33} = 1.$$

Making these substitutions and also replacing the quantities x^i_3 by their values ν^i the equations (16.20) now yield

$$g^{\alpha\beta} \, x^i_\alpha \, x^j_\beta = g^{ij} - \nu^i \nu^j. \tag{16.21}$$

The equations (16.21) are not only of interest in themselves but have certain useful applications.

17. Mixed Surface and Space Tensors. Coordinate Extension and Absolute Differentiation

Consider a tensor T such that (1) the tensor T is defined on a regular surface S in the Riemann space R and (2) the symbol for the components of T may involve both Greek and Latin indices (see Sect. 16). To avoid a multiplicity of indices in writing the components of such a mixed surface and space tensor let us select a tensor having the components $T^i_{\alpha\beta}$ as a representative tensor satisfying the above requirements. Under a transformation $u \leftrightarrow \bar{u}$ of the surface coordinates and a transformation $x \leftrightarrow \bar{x}$ of the space coordinates the components $T^i_{\alpha\beta}$ will transform by the equations

$$\bar{T}^k_{\mu\nu}(\bar{u}) = T^i_{\alpha\beta}(u) \frac{\partial u^\alpha}{\partial \bar{u}^\mu} \frac{\partial u^\beta}{\partial \bar{u}^\nu} \frac{\partial \bar{x}^k}{\partial x^i} . \tag{17.1}$$

In accordance with the transformation equations (17.1) the components $T^i_{\alpha\beta}$ will be functions of the curvilinear or surface coordinates u^α but will depend not only on the selection of the system of coordinates u^α on the surface S but also on the system of coordinates x^i selected in the Riemann space R.

To define the coordinate extensions of the tensor T and to derive the explicit formulae for the components of any extension we shall employ a system of normal coordinates y^i in the space R and also a system of normal coordinates z^α on the surface S (see Sect. 8). Assuming that each normal system has its origin at the same point P on the surface S the normal coordinates y^i and z^α will be related to the underlying coordinates x^i and u^α by the following equations

$$\left.\begin{aligned} x^i &= p^i + y^i - \frac{1}{2!}\,\Gamma^i_{jk}(p)\,y^j\,y^k - \frac{1}{3!}\,\Gamma^i_{jkm}(p)\,y^j\,y^k\,y^m - \ldots, \\ u^\alpha &= p^\alpha + z^\alpha - \frac{1}{2!}\,\Gamma^\alpha_{\beta\gamma}(p)\,z^\beta\,z^\gamma - \frac{1}{3!}\,\Gamma^\alpha_{\beta\gamma\delta}(p)\,z^\beta\,z^\gamma\,z^\delta - \ldots, \end{aligned}\right\} \tag{17.2}$$

where p^i and p^α are the coordinates of the point P in the x and u coordinate systems respectively. Also the Γ^i_{jk} are the Christoffel symbols based on the metric of the space R and correspondingly the $\Gamma^\alpha_{\beta\gamma}$ are the Christoffel symbols determined by the metric on the surface S; the remaining coefficients $\Gamma^i_{jkm}, \ldots$ and $\Gamma^\alpha_{\beta\gamma\delta}, \ldots$ which appear in (17.2) are determined as in Sect. 8. Under transformations $x \leftrightarrow \bar{x}$ and $u \leftrightarrow \bar{u}$ of the space and surface coordinates the normal coordinates y^i and z^α will transform by the linear homogeneous equations

$$y^i = a^i_k\,\bar{y}^k; \qquad a^i_k = \left(\frac{\partial x^i}{\partial \bar{x}^k}\right)_P,$$

$$z^\alpha = b^\alpha_\beta\,\bar{z}^\beta; \qquad b^\alpha_\beta = \left(\frac{\partial u^\alpha}{\partial \bar{u}^\beta}\right)_P.$$

Now denote by $t^i_{\alpha\beta}$ the components of the tensor T relative to the y,z coordinate systems and by $\bar{t}^i_{\alpha\beta}$ the components of this tensor relative to the $\bar{y},\bar{z}$ systems. Then

$$\bar{t}^i_{\alpha\beta} = t^k_{\mu\nu}\,\frac{\partial z^\mu}{\partial \bar{z}^\alpha}\,\frac{\partial z^\nu}{\partial \bar{z}^\beta}\,\frac{\partial \bar{y}^i}{\partial y^k}, \tag{17.3}$$

in which the $t^k_{\mu\nu}$ and the $\bar{t}^i_{\alpha\beta}$ are regarded as functions of the surface coordinates z^α and $\bar{z}^\alpha$ respectively. But the derivatives in (17.3) are constant. Hence if we differentiate the equations (17.3) repeatedly with respect to the variables $\bar{z}^\gamma \ldots \bar{z}^\delta$ and evaluate the resulting equations at the common origin of the normal coordinate systems we obtain

$$\bar{T}^i_{\alpha\beta,\gamma\ldots\delta}(\bar{u}) = T^k_{\mu\nu,\eta\ldots\zeta}(u)\,\frac{\partial u^\mu}{\partial \bar{u}}\,\cdots\,\frac{\partial u^\zeta}{\partial \bar{u}^\delta}\,\frac{\partial \bar{x}^i}{\partial x^k}, \tag{17.4}$$

where

$$T^k_{\mu\nu,\eta\ldots\zeta} = \left(\frac{\partial^r t^k_{\mu\nu}}{\partial z^\eta \ldots \partial z^\zeta}\right)_0, \tag{17.5}$$

and the left members of (17.4) are defined in an anologous manner. It follows from (17.4) that the quantities $T^k_{\mu\nu,\eta\ldots\zeta}$ determined by (17.5) are the components of a tensor on the surface S. We call this tensor the rth *extension* of the tensor T provided there are r indices in the set $\gamma\ldots\delta$. In particular the first extension is also called the *first covariant derivative* of T; the process of covariant differentiation can be repeated to give the second and higher covariant derivatives of the tensor T.

The formulae for the components of the above extensions are obtained by differentiation of the equations

$$t^i_{\alpha\beta} = T^k_{\mu\nu} \frac{\partial u^\mu}{\partial z^\alpha} \frac{\partial u^\nu}{\partial z^\beta} \frac{\partial y^i}{\partial x^k}, \tag{17.6}$$

followed by evaluation at the point P. Thus differentiating (17.6) with respect to the independent variables z^γ we obtain

$$\left.\begin{aligned} \frac{\partial t^i_{\alpha\beta}}{\partial z^\gamma} &= \frac{\partial T^k_{\mu\nu}}{\partial u^\eta} \frac{\partial u^\mu}{\partial z^\alpha} \frac{\partial u^\nu}{\partial z^\beta} \frac{\partial u^\eta}{\partial z^\gamma} \frac{\partial y^i}{\partial x^k} + T^k_{\mu\nu} \frac{\partial^2 u^\mu}{\partial z^\alpha \partial z^\gamma} \frac{\partial u^\nu}{\partial z^\beta} \frac{\partial y^i}{\partial x^k} \\ &+ T^k_{\mu\nu} \frac{\partial u^\mu}{\partial z^\alpha} \frac{\partial^2 u^\nu}{\partial z^\beta \partial z^\gamma} \frac{\partial y^i}{\partial x^k} + T^k_{\mu\nu} \frac{\partial u^\mu}{\partial z^\alpha} \frac{\partial u^\nu}{\partial z^\beta} \frac{\partial^2 y^i}{\partial x^k \partial x^m} \frac{\partial x^m}{\partial u^\varepsilon} \frac{\partial u^\varepsilon}{\partial z^\gamma}. \end{aligned}\right\} \tag{17.7}$$

Then, evaluating (17.7) at the point P and making use of the relations (17.2), we find that

$$T^i_{\alpha\beta,\gamma} = \frac{\partial T^i_{\alpha\beta}}{\partial u^\gamma} - T^i_{\mu\beta}\, \Gamma^\mu_{\alpha\gamma} - T^i_{\alpha\mu}\, \Gamma^\mu_{\beta\gamma} + T^k_{\alpha\beta}\, \Gamma^i_{km}\, x^m_\gamma, \tag{17.8}$$

where the quantities x^m_γ are given by (16.2). It is evident that the formulae for the covariant derivative and, more generally, for the extensions of any tensor T can be found by this process.

Now suppose that the tensor T is defined only along a curve C on the surface S. Assuming that C is determined by equations

$u^\alpha = u^\alpha(t)$ where the functions $u^\alpha(t)$ are differentiable and such that

$$g_{\alpha\beta} \frac{du^\alpha}{dt} \frac{du^\beta}{dt} > 0,$$

i.e. that the curve C is regular (cp. Sect. 6), let us differentiate the relations (17.3) repeated with respect to the parameter t and then evaluate at the point P. But this gives

$$\frac{D^r \bar{T}^i_{\alpha\beta}}{Dt^r} = \frac{D^r T^k_{\mu\nu}}{Dt^r} \frac{\partial u^\mu}{\partial \bar{u}^\alpha} \frac{\partial u^\nu}{\partial \bar{u}^\beta} \frac{\partial \bar{x}^i}{\partial x^k}, \tag{17.9}$$

where

$$\frac{D^r T^k_{\mu\nu}}{Dt^r} = \left(\frac{d^r t^k_{\mu\nu}}{dt^r} \right)_0; \qquad \frac{D^r \bar{T}^i_{\alpha\beta}}{Dt^r} = \left(\frac{d^r \bar{t}^i_{\alpha\beta}}{dt^r} \right)_0. \tag{17.10}$$

Hence the quantities defined by (17.10) along C are the components of a tensor in accordance with the equations (17.9). We call this tensor the rth *absolute extension* of the tensor T. The first absolute extension may conveniently be referred to as the *first absolute derivative*. A repetition of this process of absolute differentiation leads to second and higher order absolute derivatives which are, of course, not in general equal to the corresponding second and higher absolute extensions. The process of obtaining the formulae for these absolute derivatives and absolute extensions is analogous to the process by which we derive the formulae for the covariant derivatives and extensions of the tensor T. Thus, differentiating (17.6) with respect to the parameter t and evaluating at the point P on the curve C we obtain

$$\left. \begin{aligned} \frac{DT^i_{\alpha\beta}}{Dt} = \frac{dT^i_{\alpha\beta}}{dt} - T^i_{\mu\beta} \Gamma^\mu_{\alpha\gamma} \frac{du^\gamma}{dt} - T^i_{\alpha\mu} \Gamma^\mu_{\beta\gamma} \frac{du^\gamma}{dt} \\ + T^k_{\alpha\beta} \Gamma^i_{km} x^m_\gamma \frac{du^\gamma}{dt}, \end{aligned} \right\} \tag{17.11}$$

for the components of the first absolute derivative of the tensor T. In this connection it may be observed that the components of the absolute derivative are obtained from the components of the covariant derivative, given by (17.8), by multiplication by the derivatives du^γ/dt of the functions $u^\gamma(t)$ defining the curve C.

Remark 1. The above *surface* covariant derivative of a tensor T, defined on a regular surface S, whose symbol involves only Greek indices is identical with the covariant derivative of T considered as a tensor in a two dimensional Riemann space having the metric of the surface S; moreover the absolute derivative of such a tensor T, along a regular curve C on S, is given by

$$\frac{DT^{\alpha\ldots\beta}_{\gamma\ldots\delta}}{Dt} = T^{\alpha\ldots\beta}_{\gamma\ldots\delta,\varepsilon}\frac{du^\varepsilon}{dt},$$

where $T^{\alpha\ldots\beta}_{\gamma\ldots\delta}$ and $T^{\alpha\ldots\beta}_{\gamma\ldots\delta,\varepsilon}$ are the components of the tensor T and its covariant derivative respectively and the du^ε/dt are the derivatives of the functions $u^\varepsilon(t)$ defining the curve C. In the other extreme case where the components of T are functions of the space coordinates x^i and the symbol of the components involves only Latin indices the surface covariant derivative has components

$$T^{i\ldots j}_{k\ldots m,\alpha} = T^{i\ldots j}_{k\ldots m,r}\, x^r_\alpha, \tag{17.12}$$

where $T^{i\ldots j}_{k\ldots m}$ denotes the components of T and $T^{i\ldots j}_{k\ldots m,r}$ are the components of the *spatial* covariant derivative of T considered as a tensor in the Riemann space R. Correspondingly we have

$$\frac{DT^{i\ldots j}_{k\ldots m}}{Dt} = T^{i\ldots j}_{k\ldots m,\alpha}\frac{du^\alpha}{dt}, \tag{17.13}$$

for the components of the absolute derivative of T along a regular curve C on S.

Since the components of the spatial covariant and absolute derivatives of the metric tensor of the space R are equal to zero it follows from (17.12) and (17.13) that the components of the corresponding surface derivatives of this tensor must likewise vanish. A similar remark can be made concerning the covariant and absolute derivatives of the skew-symmetric tensor whose components are the quantities ε_{ijk} or ε^{ijk} in an oriented Riemann space R.

Remark 2. Let S be a regular oriented surface in a Riemann space R and C a regular curve on S. We assume that C is defined by equations

$u^\alpha = u^\alpha(s)$ where s denotes arc length along C. Corresponding to the results in Sect. 15 we now have the equations

$$\lambda^\alpha = \frac{du^\alpha}{ds}; \qquad g_{\alpha\beta}\,\lambda^\alpha\,\lambda^\beta = 1; \qquad g_{\alpha\beta}\,\lambda^\alpha \frac{D\lambda^\beta}{Ds} = 0. \tag{17.14}$$

The first of the equations (17.14) defines the components λ^α of a vector λ tangent to C, the second equation expresses the fact that λ is a unit vector and the third equation (17.14), which is obtained by absolute differentiation of the second equation (17.14), states that the absolute derivative of λ is perpendicular to the tangent vector λ. Hence the absolute derivative of λ is normal to the curve C. We can therefore define a unit vector μ, normal to C, by writing

$$\frac{D\lambda^\alpha}{Ds} = \sigma\mu^\alpha; \qquad \varepsilon_{\alpha\beta}\,\lambda^\alpha\,\mu^\beta = 1, \tag{17.15}$$

where σ is a scalar along the curve C and the second of these relations, which is analogous to the condition (15.11), determines the direction of the vector μ and hence the algebraic sign of the normalizing scalar σ. The vector μ is the *unit normal* to the curve C and the scalar σ is called the *geodesic curvature* of C.

We readily observe that the second equation (17.15) is equivalent to either of the following two sets of relations

$$\lambda^\alpha = g_{\beta\gamma}\,\varepsilon^{\alpha\beta}\,\mu^\gamma; \qquad \mu^\alpha = -\,g_{\beta\gamma}\,\varepsilon^{\alpha\beta}\,\lambda^\gamma. \tag{17.16}$$

By absolute differentiation of the second set of relations (17.16) along C and application of the first set of these relations it now follows that

$$\frac{D\mu^\alpha}{Ds} = -\,g_{\beta\gamma}\,\varepsilon^{\alpha\beta}\,\frac{D\lambda^\gamma}{Ds} = -\,\sigma g_{\beta\gamma}\,\varepsilon^{\alpha\beta}\,\mu^\gamma = -\,\sigma\lambda^\alpha.$$

Combining this result with the first set of equations (17.15) we obtain the following relations which are analogous to the Frenet formulae derived in Sect. 15, namely

$$\frac{D\lambda^\alpha}{Ds} = \sigma\mu^\alpha; \qquad \frac{D\mu^\alpha}{Ds} = -\,\sigma\lambda^\alpha. \tag{17.17}$$

18. Formulae of Gauss and Weingarten

It follows from the relations (16.5), by covariant differentiation, that

$$g_{ij}\, x^i_{\alpha,\gamma}\, x^j_\beta + g_{ij}\, x^i_\alpha\, x^j_{\beta,\gamma} = 0, \tag{18.1}$$

where the quantities x^i_α are given by (16.2). By cyclic permutation of the indices α,β,γ in (18.1) we can also write

$$g_{ij}\, x^i_{\beta,\alpha}\, x^j_\gamma + g_{ij}\, x^i_\beta\, x^j_{\gamma,\alpha} = 0, \tag{18.2}$$

$$g_{ij}\, x^i_{\gamma,\beta}\, x^j_\alpha + g_{ij}\, x^i_\gamma\, x^j_{\alpha,\beta} = 0. \tag{18.3}$$

But the quantities $x^i_{\alpha,\beta}$ are symmetric in the indices α and β as can immediately be seen from the formula for these components. Hence if we add the left members of (18.2) and (18.3) and then subtract the left member of (18.1) from the resulting expression we obtain

$$g_{ij}\, x^i_{\alpha,\beta}\, x^j_\gamma = 0. \tag{18.4}$$

Now for fixed values of the indices α,β the quantities $x^i_{\alpha,\beta}$ are the components of a vector in the space and the relations (18.4) express the condition that this vector is normal to the surface S. Hence we must have relations of the form

$$x^i_{\alpha,\beta} = b_{\alpha\beta}\, \nu^i, \tag{18.5}$$

where the $b_{\alpha\beta}$ are the components of a symmetric tensor defined over the surface S and the ν^i are the components of the unit normal vector to S. In fact if we multiply both members of (18.5) by $g_{ij}\nu^j$ and sum on the repeated indices we obtain

$$b_{\alpha\beta} = g_{ij}\, x^i_{\alpha,\beta}\, \nu^j.$$

The relations (18.5) are the *formulae of Gauss* and the quantities $b_{\alpha\beta}$ are commonly referred to as the coefficients of *the second fundamental form of the surface S*.

Let us now apply the process of covariant differentiation to the equations

$$g_{ij}\, \nu^i\, \nu^j = 1; \qquad g_{ij}\, x^i_\alpha\, \nu^j = 0, \tag{18.6}$$

which express the condition that ν is a unit vector normal to the surface S. We thus obtain

$$g_{ij}\, \nu^i\, \nu^j_{,\alpha} = 0, \tag{18.7}$$

$$g_{ij}\, x^i_{\alpha,\beta}\, \nu^j + g_{ij}\, x^i_\alpha\, \nu^j_{,\beta} = 0. \tag{18.8}$$

From the relations (18.7) it follows that the two space vectors having components $\nu^i_{,1}$ and $\nu^i_{,2}$ are perpendicular to the normal vector ν. Hence these vectors must be tangent to the surface S. It must therefore be possible to express either set of components $\nu^i_{,1}$ and $\nu^i_{,2}$ as a linear combination of the quantities $x^i_{,1}$ and $x^i_{,2}$ since these quantities are the components of two independent vectors tangent to the surface. This gives relations of the form

$$\nu^i_{,\alpha} = \zeta^\beta_\alpha\, x^i_\beta. \tag{18.9}$$

Eliminating the quantities $x^i_{\alpha,\beta}$ and $\nu^i_{,\alpha}$ from (18.8) by the substitutions (18.5) and (18.9) and making use of the relations (16.5) we obtain the following equations

$$b_{\alpha\beta} = -g_{\alpha\sigma}\, \zeta^\sigma_\beta. \tag{18.10}$$

By means of the equations (18.10) we can eliminate the quantities ζ^β_α from the relations (18.9). In fact if we multiply (18.10) by $g^{\alpha\tau}$ and sum on the repeated indices we find that

$$\zeta^\beta_\alpha = -g^{\beta\sigma}\, b_{\alpha\sigma}. \tag{18.11}$$

Hence, removing the quantities ζ^β_α from (18.9) by the substitution (18.11), we obtain the *formulae of Weingarten*, namely

$$\nu^i_{,\alpha} = -g^{\beta\gamma}\, b_{\alpha\beta}\, x^i_\gamma. \tag{18.12}$$

Remark. The components ν^i of the unit normal vector ν are evidently constant over a plane in the Euclidean metric space E referred to one of its cartesian coordinated systems. Hence $\nu^i_{,\alpha} = 0$ and from (18.12) we have

$$g^{\beta\gamma} b_{\alpha\beta} x^i_{\gamma} = 0. \tag{18.13}$$

Multiplying (18.13) by $g_{ij} x^j_{\varepsilon}$ and making use of (16.5) it follows that $b_{\alpha\beta} = 0$. Conversely, if $b_{\alpha\beta} = 0$ over a surface S in the space E, referred to a cartesian coordinate system, we shall have $\nu^i_{,\alpha} = 0$ from (18.12). But this condition evidently implies that S is a plane. *Hence a surface S is a plane in the Euclidean metric space E if, and only if, its second fundamental form vanishes identically.*

19. Gaussian and Mean Curvature of a Surface

Two scalars K and Ω can be defined over a regular surface S in a three dimensional Riemannian space R by the following equations

$$K = -\tfrac{1}{4}\,\varepsilon^{\alpha\beta}\,\varepsilon^{\gamma\delta}\,B_{\alpha\beta\gamma\delta}, \tag{19.1}$$

$$\Omega = \tfrac{1}{2}\,g^{\alpha\beta}\,b_{\alpha\beta}, \tag{19.2}$$

where the $B_{\alpha\beta\gamma\delta}$ are the components of the completely covariant form of the curvature tensor B (see Remark 1 in Sect. 11) and the $b_{\alpha\beta}$ are the coefficients of the second fundamental form of the surface S (see Sect. 18). The scalar K, which is an intrinsic differential invariant of the surface S, is known as the *total* or *Gaussian curvature* and the scalar Ω is the *mean curvature* of the surface.

In this connection it may be observed that the components $B_{\alpha\beta\gamma\delta}$ can be represented by writing

$$B_{\alpha\beta\gamma\delta} = -K\,\varepsilon_{\alpha\beta}\,\varepsilon_{\gamma\delta}. \tag{19.3}$$

In fact if we expand the right member of (19.1) we have

$$K = -\varepsilon^{12}\,\varepsilon^{12}\,B_{1212}, \tag{19.4}$$

on account of the skew-symmetric character of the quantities $\varepsilon^{\alpha\beta}$ and $B_{\alpha\beta\gamma\delta}$. Substituting the value of K given by (19.4) into (19.3) we see that this relation is satisfied when the indices $\alpha,\beta,\gamma,\delta$ have the values 1,2,1,2 respectively. Hence (19.3) must be satisfied for any selection of the indices $\alpha,\beta,\gamma,\delta$ in view of the skew-symmetry of the components $\varepsilon_{\alpha\beta}$ and the components of the curvature tensor B.

20. Equations of Gauss and Codazzi

To deduce other relations involving the components of the curvature tensor of the surface S and the coefficients of its second fundamental form let us consider the mixed surface and space tensor X with components x^i_α defined by (16.2). The components of the covariant derivative of this tensor are given by

$$x^i_{\alpha,\beta} = \frac{\partial x^i_\alpha}{\partial u^\beta} - x^i_\sigma \Gamma^\sigma_{\alpha\beta} + x^k_\alpha \Gamma^i_{km} x^m_\beta . \tag{20.1}$$

Transforming these relations to the normal coordinate systems y,z considered in Sect. 17, differentiating with respect to the surface coordinates z^γ and then evaluating at the common origin of the normal systems, we obtain

$$x^i_{\alpha,\beta,\gamma} = x^i_{\alpha,\beta\gamma} - A^\sigma_{\alpha\beta\gamma} x^i_\sigma + A^i_{kmr} x^i_\alpha x^m_\beta x^r_\gamma, \tag{20.2}$$

where $x^i_{\alpha,\beta,\gamma}$ and $x^i_{\alpha,\beta\gamma}$ are the components of the second covariant derivative and second extension of the tensor X and where $A^\sigma_{\alpha\beta\gamma}$ and A^i_{kmr} are the components of the first normal tensors of the surface S and the space R respectively. Interchanging the indices β,γ in (20.2) and subtracting it now follows that

$$x^i_{\alpha,\beta,\gamma} - x^i_{\alpha,\beta,\gamma} = - B^\sigma_{\alpha\beta\gamma} x^i_\sigma + B^i_{kmr} x^k_\alpha x^m_\beta x^r_\gamma, \tag{20.3}$$

on account of the relation between the components of the first normal tensor A and the curvature tensor B (see Remark 1 in Sect. 11).

By covariant differentiation of the relations (18.5) and application of (18.12) we also have

$$x^i_{\alpha,\beta,\gamma} = b_{\alpha\beta,\gamma} \nu^i - b_{\alpha\beta} g^{\sigma\tau} b_{\sigma\gamma} x^i_\tau . \tag{20.4}$$

Hence, interchanging the indices β,γ in (20.4) and subtracting, we obtain

$$x^i_{\alpha,\beta,\gamma} - x^i_{\alpha,\gamma,\beta} = (b_{\alpha\beta,\gamma} - b_{\alpha\gamma,\beta})\, \nu^i - g^{\sigma\tau}(b_{\alpha\beta}\, b_{\sigma\gamma} - b_{\alpha\gamma}\, b_{\sigma\beta})\, x^i_\tau. \quad (20.5)$$

Now one usually assumes that the surface S is immersed in a Euclidean metric space E so that the curvature tensor components B^i_{kmr} in (20.3) are equal to zero. Making this restriction and equating the right members of (20.3) and (20.5) we have the following relations

$$(b_{\alpha\beta,\gamma} - b_{\alpha\gamma,\beta})\, \nu^i + [B^\tau_{\alpha\beta\gamma} - g^{\sigma\tau}(b_{\alpha\beta}\, b_{\sigma\gamma} - b_{\alpha\gamma}\, b_{\sigma\beta})]\, x^i_\tau = 0.$$

If we multiply these equations (a) by the quantities $g_{ij}\nu^j$ and (b) by the quantities $g_{ij}x^j_\delta$ and in each case sum on the repeated indices we find that

$$b_{\alpha\beta,\gamma} - b_{\alpha\gamma,\beta} = 0, \quad (20.6)$$

$$B_{\alpha\beta\gamma\delta} = b_{\alpha\delta}\, b_{\beta\gamma} - b_{\alpha\gamma}\, b_{\beta\delta}, \quad (20.7)$$

when account is taken of the fact (1) that ν is a unit vector, (2) that ν is normal to the surface S, (3) that the quantities x^i_1 and x^i_2 are the components of spatial vectors tangent to S, and (4) that the coefficients $g_{\alpha\beta}$ of the first fundamental form of the surface S are given by the equations (16.5).

The relations (20.6) are known as the *Codazzi equations* and the relations (20.7) as the *Gauss equations* of a surface S immersed in the Euclidean metric space E.

21. Principal Curvatures and Principal Directions

Let C be a regular curve on a regular surface S in the three dimensional Euclidean metric space E. Then the spatial components λ^i and the surface components λ^α of the unit tangent vector λ to C are related by the equations

$$\lambda^i = \frac{dx^i}{ds} = \frac{\partial x^i}{\partial u^\alpha}\frac{du^\alpha}{ds} = x^i_\alpha \lambda^\alpha, \tag{21.1}$$

where s denotes arc length along C (cp. Sect. 16). By absolute differentiation of the equations (21.1) we now have

$$\frac{D\lambda^i}{Ds} = x^i_\alpha \frac{D\lambda^\alpha}{Ds} + x^i_{\alpha,\beta} \lambda^\alpha \frac{du^\beta}{ds}. \tag{21.2}$$

Hence, making the substitution (18.5) and also eliminating the derivatives in (21.2) by means of (15.14), (17.14) and (17.17), we obtain

$$\kappa \xi^i = \sigma \mu^i + (b_{\alpha\beta} \lambda^\alpha \lambda^\beta)\nu^i, \tag{21.3}$$

where the μ^i are the spatial components of the tangent vector μ to the surface. Multiplying (21.3) by $g_{ij}\nu^j$ and summing on repeated indices we have

$$(g_{ij}\, \nu^i\, \xi^j)\kappa = b_{\alpha\beta} \lambda^\alpha \lambda^\beta. \tag{21.4}$$

Let us now assume that the curve C is the intersection of the surface S and a plane through the normal ν at an arbitrary point P of S. The vector ξ will then be normal to the surface S at P as is clear from the discussion in the Remark 2 of Sect. 15. Hence at P the unit vector ξ must be identical with the unit normal vector ν or ξ must have a direction opposite to that of ν. The coefficient of κ in (21.4) will therefore have the value ± 1 at the point P and hence, at P, this equation becomes

$$\pm \kappa = b_{\alpha\beta} \lambda^\alpha \lambda^\beta. \tag{21.5}$$

The quantity in the right member of (21.5) is called the *normal curvature* of the surface S in the direction λ at the point P. Denoting the normal curvature by κ_n we therefore have

$$\kappa_n = b_{\alpha\beta} \lambda^\alpha \lambda^\beta. \tag{21.6}$$

As so defined the normal curvature $\kappa_n = \pm \kappa$ at the point P; hence the normal curvature can have a positive or a negative value.

The normal curvature κ_n at a point P of the surface S will have a *stationary value*, e.g. a relative maximum or minimum, for a specified direction λ provided that

$$b_{\alpha\beta} \lambda^\alpha \delta\lambda^\beta = 0; \qquad g_{\alpha\beta} \lambda^\alpha \delta\lambda^\beta = 0. \tag{21.7}$$

In other words the unit vector λ whose components occur in (21.7) will determine a stationary value of κ_n if the first equation (21.7) is satisfied for all variations $\delta\lambda^\beta$ which satisfy the second equation (21.7). Obviously the first condition (21.7) can be replaced by

$$(b_{\alpha\beta} \lambda^\alpha - \kappa_n g_{\alpha\beta} \lambda^\alpha) \delta\lambda^\beta = 0. \tag{21.8}$$

Now if $g_{\alpha 1}\lambda^\alpha \neq 0$ at the point P, which is always possible by a suitable choice of the coordinates u^α, we can suppose that $\delta\lambda^2$ is arbitrary and we can then determine the value of $\delta\lambda^1$ by solution of the second equation (21.7). With this understanding let us choose the quantity κ_n in (21.8) so that the parenthesis expression in this equation vanishes for $\beta = 1$; but then this expression must also vanish for $\beta = 2$ since the variation $\delta\lambda^2$ is arbitrary. Hence we shall have

$$(b_{\alpha\beta} - \kappa_n g_{\alpha\beta}) \lambda^\beta = 0. \tag{21.9}$$

If we multiply (21.9) by the components λ^α of the unit vector λ and sum on the repeated indices we immediately obtain the equation (21.6); hence the quantity κ_n in (21.9) must be the normal curvature associated with the direction λ.

Now the determinant of the coefficients of the λ^β in (21.9) must vanish; this leads to an equation for the stationary values of κ_n which can be written in the form

$$\kappa_n^2 - g^{\alpha\beta} b_{\alpha\beta} \kappa_n + \frac{b}{g} = 0, \tag{21.10}$$

where b and g denote the determinants $|b_{\alpha\beta}|$ and $|g_{\alpha\beta}|$ respectively. Also, combining the equations (19.3) and (20.7), we have

$$K \varepsilon_{\alpha\beta} \varepsilon_{\gamma\delta} = b_{\alpha\gamma} b_{\beta\delta} - b_{\alpha\delta} b_{\beta\gamma}. \tag{21.11}$$

Hence if we choose the indices $\alpha,\beta,\gamma,\delta$ in (21.11) to have the values 1,2,1,2 respectively and then replace the quantity ε_{12} in the resulting equation by the value given in Remark 4 of Sect. 6 we find that

$$K = \frac{b}{g}\cdot \tag{21.12}$$

Making use of (19.2) and (21.12) the equation (21.10) can now be written

$$\kappa_n^2 - 2\,\Omega \kappa_n + K = 0. \tag{21.13}$$

The two solutions κ_n of the equation (21.13) are called the *principal curvatures* and the directions or unit vectors λ associated with these solutions κ_n are called the *principal directions* of the surface S at the point P. Denoting the principal curvatures by κ_1 and κ_2 we therefore have

$$K = \kappa_1 \kappa_2; \qquad \Omega = \tfrac{1}{2}(\kappa_1 + \kappa_2). \tag{21.14}$$

Hence the Gaussian curvature K of a regular surface S in a Euclidean metric space of three dimensions is equal to the product of the principal curvatures and the mean curvature Ω is equal to one-half the sum of the principal curvatures.

Remark. Choose a system of coordinates u^α such that $g_{\alpha\beta} = \delta_{\alpha\beta}$ at a point P of the surface S. The condition that λ is a unit vector at P is then given by

$$(\lambda^1)^2 + (\lambda^2)^2 = 1. \tag{21.15}$$

Regarding the components λ^α of λ as the coordinates of a rectangular system the equation (21.15) defines a unit circle. Denote the set of points comprising this circle by Σ. Then any unit vector λ determines a point p of the set Σ and conversely any point p of Σ determines a unit vector λ. Hence the normal curvature κ_n given by (21.6) can be thought of as a point function defined over the set Σ and is, in fact, evidently a continuous function of the points p of this set. The function κ_n will therefore assume its maximum value κ_1 at some point p_1 and its minimum value κ_2 at some point p_2 of the set Σ. These maximum and minimum values will be stationary values of the function κ_n and hence, as indicated, can be identified with the stationary values κ_1 and κ_2 in the above discussion.

One or the other of the following cases must now occur

Case (α) $\quad \kappa_n = 0$, *for all* $p \subset \Sigma$,

Case (β) $\quad \kappa_n =$ *const.* $(\neq 0)$, *over* Σ,

Case (γ) $\quad \kappa_n \neq$ *const., over* Σ.

Corresponding to these cases the above maximum and minimum values of the function κ_n on the set Σ must be such that

$$(\alpha) \quad \kappa_1 = \kappa_2 = 0; \qquad (\beta) \quad \kappa_1 = \kappa_2 \neq 0; \qquad (\gamma) \quad \kappa_1 > \kappa_2.$$

In treating Case (α) and Case (β) it will be helpful to suppose that λ^α is represented by writing $\lambda^1 = \cos\theta$ and $\lambda^2 = \sin\theta$. Then we shall have

$$b_{\alpha\beta}\,\lambda^\alpha\,\lambda^\beta = b_{11}\cos^2\theta + 2\,b_{12}\sin\theta\cos\theta + b_{22}\sin^2\theta. \tag{21.16}$$

Equating to zero the expression in the right member of (21.16) and dividing by $\cos^2\theta$ we obtain

$$b_{22}\tan^2\theta + 2\,b_{12}\tan\theta + b_{11} = 0, \tag{21.17}$$

under the condition of Case (α). But it follows from (21.17) that $b_{11} = b_{12} = b_{22} = 0$; in other words all quantities $b_{\alpha\beta}$ must vanish. A point P on the surface S at which all components $b_{\alpha\beta}$ are equal to zero may be called a *flat point* and at such a point the normal curvature is zero for every direction λ. From the result in the Remark in Sect. 18 we see that *a plane is the only surface composed entirely of flat points.*

Turning next to Case (β) it follows from (21.6) and (21.16) that

$$b_{11} \cos^2 \theta + 2\, b_{12} \sin \theta \cos \theta + b_{22} \sin^2 \theta = \text{const.} \tag{21.18}$$

Since (12.18) is an identity in θ it can be differentiated with respect to θ; this gives a condition which can be written in the form

$$b_{12} \tan^2 \theta + (b_{11} - b_{22}) \tan \theta - b_{12} = 0.$$

Hence we must have $b_{12} = 0$ and $b_{11} = b_{22}$. Putting b_{11} and b_{22} equal to k we now see that

$$b = k\, g_{\alpha\beta}, \qquad (k \neq 0), \tag{21.19}$$

at the point P; evidently the proportionality factor k in this relation must be different from zero since otherwise the condition of Case (α) would be satisfied. A point P at which the condition (21.19) holds is called an *umbilical point*. It is interesting to observe in this connection that if we multiply (21.19) by $g^{\alpha\beta}$ and sum on the repeated indices we find that $k = \Omega$ on account of (19.2). Hence the condition (21.19) can be replaced by

$$b_{\alpha\beta} = \Omega\, g_{\alpha\beta}; \qquad \Omega \neq 0. \tag{21.20}$$

Let us now substitute the values of the quantities $b_{\alpha\beta}$ given by (21.20) into the equations (20.6) under the assumption that the condition (21.20) holds at every point of a surface S in the Euclidean metric space. This gives us the relations

$$g_{\alpha\beta}\, \Omega_{,\gamma} - g_{\alpha\gamma}\, \Omega_{,\beta} = 0. \tag{21.21}$$

Then multiplying (21.21) by $g^{\alpha\beta}$ and summing on the repeated indices we find that $\Omega_{,\alpha} = 0$. Hence the mean curvature Ω is constant over the surface S. Now eliminate the quantities $b_{\alpha\beta}$ between (18.12) and (21.20). We thus obtain

$$\nu^i_{,\alpha} + \Omega x^i_{\alpha} = (\nu^i + \Omega x^i)_{,\alpha} = 0, \tag{21.22}$$

over S. Integrating (21.22) we have

$$\nu^i = -\Omega(x^i - a^i), \tag{21.23}$$

where the a^i are constants of integration. Substituting the values of the ν^i into the equation

$$g_{ij}\, \nu^i \nu^j = 1,$$

which expresses the condition that ν is a unit vector in the Euclidean metric space referred to a system of cartesian coordinates, we now find that

$$g_{ij}(x^i - a^i)(x^j - a^j) = b^2, \tag{21.24}$$

where $b^2 = 1/\Omega^2$. But (21.24) is, by definition, the equation of a sphere of radius b and center at the point with coordinates a^i in the Euclidean metric space. *Hence a sphere is the only surface, composed entirely of umbilical points, in the Euclidean metric space E.*

Under the condition of Case (γ) we have $\kappa_1 > \kappa_2$ where κ_1 and κ_2 are the maximum and minimum values respectively of the function κ_n on the set Σ. Denoting by λ_1 and λ_2 the directions or unit vectors λ associated with the values κ_1 and κ_2 and by λ_1^α and λ_2^α the components of these vectors, the following relations must be satisfied, namely

$$(b_{\alpha\beta} - \kappa_1 g_{\alpha\beta})\lambda_1^\beta = 0, \tag{21.25}$$

$$(b_{\alpha\beta} - \kappa_2 g_{\alpha\beta})\lambda_2^\beta = 0. \tag{21.26}$$

Multiplying (21.25) by λ_2^α and (21.26) by λ_1^α and then subtracting the resulting equations we obtain

$$(\kappa_1 - \kappa_2)g_{\alpha\beta}\lambda_1^\alpha \lambda_2^\beta = 0. \tag{21.27}$$

But, since the values κ_1 and κ_2 are distinct, it follows from (21.27) that

$$g_{\alpha\beta}\lambda_1^\alpha \lambda_2^\beta = 0. \tag{21.28}$$

The condition (21.28) implies that the principal directions λ_1 and λ_2 are perpendicular. Moreover the directions λ_1 and λ_2 are the only principal directions at the point P. This follows from the fact that the equation (21.13) has at most two solutions which must be given by the above maximum and minimum values κ_1 and κ_2 of the function κ_n; hence any other principal direction λ would have to be perpendicular to one of the mutually perpendicular directions λ_1 or λ_2 in consequence of an equation of the form (21.27) in which the values κ_1 and κ_2 are distinct.

A curve C on the surface S such that at each point of C the unit tangent vector can be identified with the vector λ giving one of the principal directions is called a *line of curvature* of the surface. Hence in general, i.e. when Case (γ) of the above Remark applies, there can be at most two families of lines of curvature on the surface S and these families will be orthogonal.

22. Asymptotic Lines

A regular curve C on the surface S is called an *asymptotic line* if the equation

$$b_{\alpha\beta}\,\lambda^\alpha\,\lambda^\beta = 0, \tag{22.1}$$

is satisfied along C, where the $b_{\alpha\beta}$ are the coefficients of the second fundamental form of the surface and the λ^α are the components of the unit tangent vector λ to C. Now along an asymptotic line L the equation (21.3) reduces to

$$\kappa\xi^i = \sigma\mu^i. \tag{22.2}$$

Hence the components of the vectors ξ and μ are proportional; but this implies that $\xi^i = \pm\,\mu^i$ since ξ and μ are unit vectors; hence $\kappa = \pm\,\sigma$, i.e. the curvature κ and the geodesic curvature σ of an asymptotic line are equal in magnitude. The principal normal ξ is therefore tangent to the surface S and hence the binormal ζ must be normal to S along an asymptotic line L.

Remark. As observed above we must have

$$\zeta^i = \pm\,\nu^i, \tag{22.3}$$

along an asymptotic line L, where ζ is the binormal to L and ν is the unit normal vector to the surface. By absolute differentiation of (22.3) with respect to the arc length s along L and use of the relations (15.14) we obtain

$$\tau\xi^i = \pm\,\frac{D\nu^i}{Ds} = \pm\,\nu^i{}_{,\alpha}\,\lambda^\alpha. \tag{22.4}$$

Continuing we deduce the following two sets of relations, namely

$$\tau^2 = g_{ij}\,\nu^i_{,\alpha}\,\nu^j_{,\beta}\,\lambda^\alpha\,\lambda^\beta, \tag{22.5}$$

$$\tau^2 = g^{\mu\nu}\,b_{\mu\alpha}\,b_{\nu\beta}\,\lambda^\alpha\,\lambda^\beta. \tag{22.6}$$

The equation (22.5) is obtained from (22.4) by an obvious formal operation plus the fact that ξ is a unit vector. Elimination of the quantities $\nu^i_{,\alpha}$ in (22.5) by means of the relations (18.12) and use of the equations (16.5) for the components $g_{\alpha\beta}$ leads immediately to the equation (22.6).

When we multiply both members of the equations (21.11) by $g^{\alpha\delta}\,\lambda^\beta\,\lambda^\gamma$ and sum on repeated indices we find that

$$(g^{\alpha\delta}\,\varepsilon_{\alpha\beta}\,\varepsilon_{\gamma\delta}\,\lambda^\beta\,\lambda^\gamma)\,K = g^{\alpha\delta}\,b_{\alpha\gamma}\,b_{\beta\delta}\,\lambda^\beta\,\lambda^\gamma, \tag{22.7}$$

when account is taken of the condition (22.1) along the asymptotic line. But one can readily observe that the expression in parenthesis in the left member of (22.7) is equal to -1. Hence when we subtract corresponding members of the equations (22.6) and (22.7) we are led to the following simple equation due to Enneper, namely

$$\tau = \pm\sqrt{-K},$$

by which the torsion τ of an asymptotic line is related to the Gaussian curvature K of the surface.

23. Orthogonal Ennuples and Normal Congruences

Let $\lambda_{(1)}$, $\lambda_{(2)}$ and $\lambda_{(3)}$ be a set of three mutually perpendicular unit vectors in a Riemann space R of three dimensions. Such a set of vectors will be referred to as an *orthogonal ennuple.* Representing the vectors of an orthogonal ennuple by their contravariant components $\lambda^i_{(1)}$, $\lambda^i_{(2)}$ and $\lambda^i_{(3)}$ we must therefore have

$$g_{ij}\, \lambda^i_{(p)}\, \lambda^j_{(q)} = \delta_{pq}, \tag{23.1}$$

where the g_{ij} are the components of the fundamental metric tensor of R. If $\lambda_{(p)i} = g_{ij}\lambda^j_{(p)}$ are the covariant components of the vector $\lambda_{(p)}$ it follows readily from (23.1) that

$$g_{ij} = \lambda_{(p)i}\, \lambda_{(p)j}; \qquad \lambda^i_{(p)}\, \lambda_{(p)j} = \delta^i_j, \tag{23.2}$$

where the index p is summed over the values 1,2,3. Also, corresponding to the first equation (23.2), one can easily show that the components g^{ij} of the contravariant form of the metric tensor of the space R are given by

$$g^{ij} = \lambda^i_{(p)}\, \lambda^j_{(p)}. \tag{23.3}$$

Either set of equations (23.2), or the set of equations (23.3), is equivalent to the equations (23.1) which express the conditions that the vectors $\lambda_{(p)}$ are unit vectors and mutually perpendicular in the space R.

A vector field λ defined in the Riemann space R will determine a *congruence of curves* in R as solutions of the system of differential equations

$$\frac{dx^i}{dt} = \lambda^i(x). \tag{23.4}$$

Evidently the space R will be covered completely by the curves of this congruence and there will be one, and only one, curve of the congruence passing through any given point P of R. The congruence will be said to be *normal* provided there exists a family of surfaces

$$f(x^1,x^2,x^3) = \text{const.}, \tag{23.5}$$

which have the curves of the congruence as their orthogonal trajectories. We shall now investigate the condition under which one of the vectors $\lambda_{(p)}$ of the above orthogonal ennuple will determine a normal congruence.

For definiteness let us consider the congruence C_3 determined by the vector $\lambda_{(3)}$. Now it was observed in Remark 1 of Sect. 16 that the derivatives $\partial f/\partial x^i$ are the components of a covariant vector perpendicular to a surface (23.5). If the family of surfaces (23.5) has the curves of the congruence C_3 as its orthogonal trajectories the vectors $\lambda_{(1)}$ and $\lambda_{(2)}$ at any point P of R must therefore be tangent to the surface (23.5) which passes through the point P. Hence we must have

$$X_r(f) \equiv \lambda^i_{(r)} \frac{\partial f}{\partial x^i} = 0, \qquad (r = 1,2), \tag{23.6}$$

as the condition for the congruence C_3 to be normal. In other words the function $f(x)$ which determines the family of surfaces (23.5) having the curves of the congruence C_3 as its orthogonal trajectories must be given as a solution of the system of differential equations (23.6).

The differential equations (23.6) will admit a solution $f(x)$ determining the required family of surfaces (23.5) if, and only if, the equations (23.6) form a *complete system* and the condition for these equations to be complete is that the quantities $(X_q,X_r)f$ defined by

$$(X_q, X_r)f = X_q X_r(f) - X_r X_q(f) \tag{23.7}$$

are expressible linearly and homogeneously for $q,r = 1,2$ in terms of the quantities $X_1(f)$ and $X_2(f)$. Now

$$X_q X_r(f) = \frac{\partial^2 f}{\partial x^i \partial x^j} \lambda^i_{(q)} \lambda^j_{(r)} + \frac{\partial \lambda^j_{(r)}}{\partial x^i} \frac{\partial f}{\partial x^j} \lambda^i_{(q)}. \tag{23.8}$$

These expressions for the scalar quantities $X_q X_r(f)$ are evidently invariant under coordinate transformations in the space R. Hence if we transform (23.8) to a system of normal coordinates (see Sect. 9) and evaluate at the origin of the normal system we obtain

$$X_q X_r (f) = f_{,ij} \lambda^i_{(q)} \lambda^j_{(r)} + \lambda^j_{(r),i} f_{,j} \lambda^i_{(q)}, \tag{23.9}$$

where the $f_{,ij}$ and $\lambda^j_{(r),i}$ are the components of the second extension of the scalar function f and the covariant derivative of the vector $\lambda_{(r)}$ respectively; the quantities $f_{,j}$ in the above equations (23.9) are the coordinate derivatives $\partial f/\partial x^j$ of the function f. Hence (23.7) becomes

$$(X_q, X_r) f = \lambda^j_{(r),i} f_{,j} \lambda^i_{(q)} - \lambda^j_{(q),i} f_{,j} \lambda^i_{(r)}. \tag{23.10}$$

In the further investigation of the equations (23.10) it will be helpful to consider the following two sets of relations, namely

$$\gamma_{pqr} = \lambda_{(p)i,j} \lambda^i_{(q)} \lambda^j_{(r)}, \tag{23.11}$$

$$\lambda^i_{(p),j} = \gamma_{pqr} \lambda^i_{(q)} \lambda_{(r)j}. \tag{23.12}$$

The quantities γ_{pqr} are scalars and are defined by (23.11) in terms of the vectors $\lambda_{(p)}$ and their covariant derivatives. The relations (23.12) express the components of the covariant derivatives of the vectors $\lambda_{(p)}$ in terms of the vectors $\lambda_{(p)}$ and the scalars γ_{pqr}; these equations are readily obtained by solving (23.11) for the components of the covariant derivatives of the vectors $\lambda_{(p)}$. Actually the quantities γ_{pqr} are not algebraically independent but must satisfy the set of relations

$$\gamma_{pqr} = \gamma_{qpr}. \tag{23.13}$$

In fact if we differentiate the equations (23.1) covariantly we obtain a set of equations which can be written in the form

$$\lambda_{(p)i,j}\,\lambda^i_{(q)} + \lambda_{(q)i,j}\,\lambda^i_{(p)} = 0.$$

Multiplying these equations by $\lambda^j_{(r)}$ and summing on the repeated index j we are led to the equations (23.13).

Eliminating the components $\lambda^j_{(r),i}$ and $\lambda^l_{(q),i}$ by substitutions of the type (23.12) and making use of the equations (23.1) as well as the identities (23.13) we find that the equations (23.10) become

$$(X_q, X_r)f = (\gamma_{mrq} - \gamma_{mqr})X_m(f) + (\gamma_{3rq} - \gamma_{3qr})X_3(f), \qquad (23.14)$$

where the indices m,q,r have the values 1,2 and there is a summation on the repeated index m over these values.

Since the determinant $|\lambda^i_{(p)}|$ does not vanish, e.g. it follows that $|\lambda^i_{(p)}| \neq 0$ from (23.1), the expressions $X_1(f)$, $X_2(f)$ and $X_3(f)$ must be linearly independent. Hence the system of differential equations (23.6) will be complete if, and only if, the coefficients of $X_3(f)$ in the right member of (23.14) are equal to zero. But since the indices r and q in (23.14) are restricted to the values 1,2 the vanishing of these coefficients produces the single relation

$$\gamma_{312} = \gamma_{321}. \qquad (23.15)$$

In other words a necessary and sufficient condition for the congruence C_3 *to be normal is that the condition* (23.15) *be satisfied.*

Remark 1. The above discussion is evidently applicable to a Riemann space of any dimensionality $n \geqslant 2$ and, for such a space, one is led to a set of equations corresponding to (23.15), namely

$$\gamma_{nqr} = \gamma_{nrq} \qquad (q,r = 1,\ldots,n-1),$$

as the conditions for the normality of the congruence C_n determined by the vector $\lambda_{(n)}$ of the set of n mutually orthogonal unit vectors $\lambda_{(p)}$. In the special case $n = 2$ the above condition is automatically satisfied corresponding to the fact that the curves of the congruence determined by either vector of the orthogonal ennuple have the curves of the congruence determined by the other vector of the ennuple as their orthogonal trajectories.

To treat the two dimensional problem specifically let λ be a vector field in a Riemann space R of two dimensions and denote by C the congruence of curves in R which are determined by solution of the differential equations (23.4). Assuming R to be *oriented* we can define a vector ξ having the covariant components $\xi_i = \varepsilon_{ij}\,\lambda^j$ and hence

$$\xi_i\,\lambda^i = \varepsilon_{ij}\,\lambda^i\,\lambda^j = 0,$$

i.e. the vectors ξ and λ are perpendicular. Hence a congruence of curves, orthogonal to the above congruence C, will be determined as a solution of the differential equations

$$\frac{dx^i}{dt} = \xi^i(x).$$

This geometrical result is obviously independent of the orientation of the space R which was assumed merely for convenience in defining the vector ξ. *Hence any congruence of curves in a two dimensional Riemann space will admit an orthogonal congruence.*

Remark 2. Let $\lambda(x)$ denote a vector field in a three dimensional Riemann space R and consider the congruence C determined by λ as a solution of the differential equations (23.4). As in the above Remark 1 we shall assume that R is oriented for convenience in defining certain vectors, associated with the vector λ, but it will be evident that the final geometrical results will be independent of the orientation of the space. We shall now derive the explicit conditions for C to be a normal congruence.

If (23.5) is a family of surfaces having the curves of the congruence C as its normal trajectories we must have

$$\frac{\partial f}{\partial x^j} = \phi\lambda_j, \tag{23.16}$$

where ϕ is a scalar function in R. By covariant differentiation of (23.16) we obtain

$$f_{,jk} = \phi_{,k}\,\lambda_j + \phi\lambda_{j,k}, \tag{23.17}$$

where the components $f_{,jk}$ are symmetric in the indices j,k and the other quantities $\phi_{,k}$ and $\lambda_{j,k}$ are the components of covariant derivatives as indicated. Multiplying (23.17) by the quantities $e^{ijk}\,\lambda_i$ and summing on repeated indices we find that

$$e^{ijk}\,\lambda_i\,\lambda_{j,k} = 0, \tag{23.18}$$

in which the e^{ijk} are the components of the skew-symmetric tensor defined in Sect. 4. *Hence* (23.18) *is a necessary condition for the congruence C to be normal.*

Now define a set of three unit vectors $\lambda_{(p)}$ in R as follows

$$\lambda^i_{(3)} = \frac{\lambda^i}{\sqrt{g_{ab}\,\lambda^a\,\lambda^b}}, \tag{23.19}$$

$$\lambda^i_{(2)} = \frac{\varepsilon^{ijk}\,\lambda_{j,k}}{\sqrt{g_{ab}\,\varepsilon^{amn}\,\lambda_{m,n}\,\varepsilon^{buv}\,\lambda_{u,v}}}, \tag{23.20}$$

$$\lambda^i_{(1)} = \varepsilon^{ijk}\,\lambda_{(2)j}\,\lambda_{(3)k}, \tag{23.21}$$

where the ε^{ijk} are the components of the skew-symmetric tensor introduced in Sect. 6. As so defined the vectors $\lambda_{(2)}$ and $\lambda_{(3)}$ are immediately seen to be unit vectors and it follows readily by recourse to the equations (6.16) that $\lambda_{(1)}$ is also a unit vector. Moreover the vectors $\lambda_{(2)}$ and $\lambda_{(3)}$ are perpendicular on account of the condition (23.18) while the vector $\lambda_{(1)}$ is perpendicular to the vectors $\lambda_{(2)}$ and $\lambda_{(3)}$ by construction. Hence the vectors $\lambda_{(1)}$, $\lambda_{(2)}$ and $\lambda_{(3)}$ form an orthogonal ennuple in the space R.

Since the given vector λ and the unit vector $\lambda_{(3)}$ defined by (23.19) determine the same congruence C it follows that C will be a normal congruence if, and only if, the condition (23.15) is satisfied where the quantities γ are constructed from the orthogonal ennuple $\lambda_{(p)}$ defined by (23.19), (23.20) and (23.21). But, using the expression (23.19) for the components of $\lambda_{(3)}$ and taking account of the fact that the vectors $\lambda_{(p)}$ are mutually perpendicular, we see that the condition (23.15) becomes

$$\lambda_{i,j}\,\lambda^i_{(1)}\,\lambda^j_{(2)} = \lambda_{i,j}\,\lambda^i_{(2)}\,\lambda^j_{(1)}. \tag{23.22}$$

Now substitute the expressions for $\lambda^i_{(2)}$ and $\lambda^i_{(1)}$ given by (23.20) and (23.21) into the relation (23.22). Cancelling certain common factors from the terms of the resulting equation, as is evidently permissible, we obtain an equation which can be written

$$\lambda_{i,j}(g_{ab}\,\varepsilon^{air}\,\varepsilon^{bpq})\,\varepsilon^{jmn}\,\lambda_{p,q}\,\lambda_{m,n}\,\lambda_r = \lambda_{i,j}(g_{ab}\,\varepsilon^{ajk}\,\varepsilon^{bpq})\,\varepsilon^{imn}\,\lambda_{p,q}\,\lambda_{m,n}\,\lambda_r. \tag{23.23}$$

Next, replacing the parenthesis expressions in (23.23) by the expressions given by the identities (6.16), we find that the equation (23.23) can be put into the following form

$$(\varepsilon^{imn}\,H_{ij}\,H_{mn})\,H_{pq}\,g^{jp}\,\lambda^q = 0, \tag{23.24}$$

in which the H's are the skew-symmetric quantities defined by

$$H_{ij} = \lambda_{i,j} - \lambda_{j,i}.$$

But the parenthesis expressions in (23.24) are readily seen to vanish by taking the index $j = 1,2,3$ in turn and performing the indicated summations. Hence (23.15) is satisfied and we have proved the following result. *The congruence of curves determined by a vector field* λ *in a three dimensional Riemann space will be normal,* i.e. *there will exist a one parameter family of surfaces* (23.5) *having the curves of the congruence as their orthogonal trajectories if, and only if, the condition* (23.18) *is satisfied.*

24. Families of Parallel Surfaces

Consider a regular surface S in a three dimensional Euclidean metric space E referred to a system of rectangular coordinates x^i and erect the normals N to the surface S as shown in Fig. 5. Denote by $\bar{S}$ the surface obtained by laying off equal distances σ along the normals N in the direction of the unit normal to S. Such a surface $\bar{S}$ is said to be *parallel* to the surface S. The surface $\bar{S}$ is determined by equations of the form

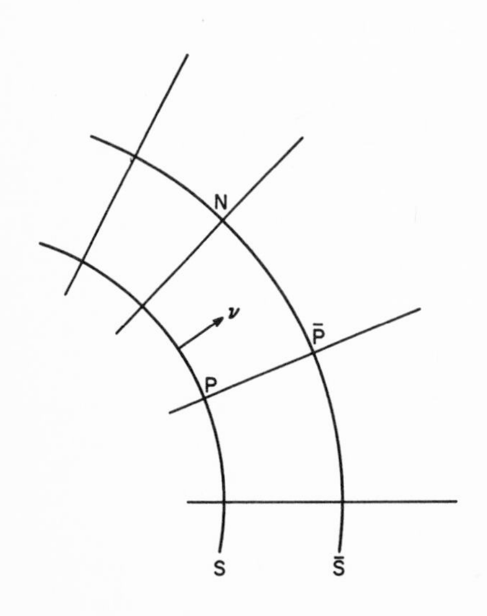

Fig. 5

$$\bar{x}^i = x^i + \sigma \nu^i, \qquad (24.1)$$

where x^i and $\bar{x}^i$ are the coordinates of corresponding points P and $\bar{P}$ of the surfaces S and $\bar{S}$, i.e. points lying on the same normal N (see Fig. 5); it is to be understood that x^i and ν^i are functions of the curvilinear coordinates u^α of the point P, i.e. the x^i are given by the equations (16.1) defining the surface S and the ν^i by one of the two sets of equations (16.11). Since the surface S is regular by hypothesis the surface $\bar{S}$ will evidently be regular for sufficiently small values of the constant σ in (24.1). We shall assume in the following discussion that the value of σ does not exceed the limit beyond which the surface S will fail to be regular.

Denoting by ν_i the covariant components of the unit normal to S at the point P we have

$$\bar{x}^i_\alpha \nu_i = x^i_\alpha \nu_i + \sigma \nu^i_{,\alpha} \nu_i, \tag{24.2}$$

when we replace the $\bar{x}^i_\alpha$ by the values obtained by differentiating the equations (24.1) with respect to the curvilinear coordinates u^α. But the first term in the right member of (24.2) vanishes since the vectors having the components x^i_1 and x^i_2 are tangent to the surface S and the second term also vanishes since ν is a unit vector. Hence we must have the following two sets of relations

$$\bar{x}^i_\alpha \nu_i = 0; \qquad \bar{x}^i_\alpha \bar{\nu}_i = 0, \tag{24.3}$$

where the $\bar{\nu}_i$ are the components of the unit normal at $\bar{P}$. Now since $\bar{S}$ is regular the matrix $||\bar{x}^i_\alpha||$ will have rank 2. Hence the components ν_i and $\bar{\nu}_i$ must have the same values to within a factor of multiplication as a consequence of the equations (24.3); but this implies that $\bar{\nu}_i$ must be equal to ν_i to within algebraic sign since ν and $\bar{\nu}$ are unit vectors. Finally if we assume the $\bar{\nu}_i$ to be continuous functions of the distance σ in the equations (24.1) we obtain the exact equality of the components of the unit normal vectors ν and $\bar{\nu}$ at the points P and $\bar{P}$ respectively.

It is clear from the above discussion that the normal line L to S at the point P is also normal to the surface $\bar{S}$ at the point $\bar{P}$. Hence one can reach the surface S by moving equal distances from the surface $\bar{S}$ along the normal lines L, i.e. the surface S is also parallel to the surface $\bar{S}$. If $S(\sigma)$ denotes the one parameter family of surfaces obtained by varying the distance σ in the equations (24.1) it is now evident that any two surfaces of this family must be mutually parallel and in this sense we can speak of $S(\sigma)$ as a family of parallel surfaces without further qualification.

To determine an expression for the components $\bar{g}_{\alpha\beta}$ of the fundamental metric tensor of the above surface $\bar{S}$ in terms of the basic invariants of the surface S let us begin with the relation

$$\bar{g}_{\alpha\beta} = \bar{x}^i_\alpha \bar{x}^i_\beta = (x^i_\alpha + \sigma \nu^i_{,\alpha})(x^i_\beta + \sigma \nu^i_{,\beta}), \tag{24.4}$$

by which the components $\bar{g}_{\alpha\beta}$ are defined (see Sect. 16). For definiteness let us think of the quantities $\bar{g}_{\alpha\beta}$ in the left member of (24.4) as associated with the point $\bar{P}$ of the surface $\bar{S}$. Then, expanding the right member of (24.4) it is easily seen that the resulting equation can be written in the form

$$\bar{g}_{\alpha\beta} = g_{\alpha\beta} - 2\,\sigma b_{\alpha\beta} + \sigma^2 \nu^i_{,\alpha}\, \nu^i_{,\beta}, \tag{24.5}$$

where $g_{\alpha\beta}$ and $b_{\alpha\beta}$ are the coefficients of the first and second fundamental forms of the surface S at the point P. Making use of the equations (18.12) we now have

$$\nu^i_{,\alpha}\, \nu^i_{,\beta} = g^{\gamma\delta}\, b_{\alpha\gamma}\, x^i_\delta\, g^{\xi\zeta}\, b_{\beta\xi}\, x^i_\zeta = b_{\alpha\xi}\, b_{\beta\zeta}\, g^{\xi\zeta}. \tag{24.6}$$

Also if we multiply both members of the equation (21.11) by $g^{\alpha\delta}$, sum on the repeated indices, and make use of the second set of identities (6.15) we find that

$$b_{\alpha\xi}\, b_{\beta\zeta}\, g^{\xi\zeta} = 2\,\Omega\, b_{\alpha\beta} - K\, g_{\alpha\beta}, \tag{24.7}$$

where K and Ω are the Gaussian and mean curvatures of the surface S at the point P. Taking account of (24.6) and (24.7) the equations (24.5) can now be written

$$\bar{g}_{\alpha\beta} = (1 - \sigma^2 K)\, g_{\alpha\beta} - 2\,\sigma\,(1 - \sigma\Omega)\, b_{\alpha\beta}. \tag{24.8}$$

The relations (24.8) *give the components $\bar{g}_{\alpha\beta}$ at the point $\bar{P}$ of the surface $\bar{S}$ in terms of the Gaussian curvature K, the mean curvature Ω, and the coefficients of the first and second fundamental forms,* i.e. *the quantities $g_{\alpha\beta}$ and $b_{\alpha\beta}$ respectively, at the point P of the surface S.*

By second covariant differentiation of (24.1) and use of the equations (18.5) we have

$$\bar{b}_{\alpha\beta}\, \bar{\nu}^i = b_{\alpha\beta}\, \nu^i + \sigma \nu^i_{,\alpha,\beta}. \tag{24.9}$$

But $\nu^i = \bar{\nu}^i$ as observed above and hence when we multiply the two members of (24.9) by ν^i and sum on the repeated index i we obtain

$$\bar{b}_{\alpha\beta} = b_{\alpha\beta} + \sigma \nu^i\, \nu^i_{,\alpha,\beta} = b_{\alpha\beta} - \sigma \nu^i_{,\alpha}\, \nu^i_{,\beta}. \tag{24.10}$$

We now modify the right members of (24.10) by use of the equations (24.6) and (24.7) corresponding to our previous treatment of the equations (24.5). *Hence we obtain*

$$\bar{b}_{\alpha\beta} = (1 - 2\,\sigma\Omega)\, b_{\alpha\beta} + \sigma K g_{\alpha\beta} \tag{24.11}$$

as the equations for the determination of the coefficients $\bar{b}_{\alpha\beta}$ *of the second fundamental form of the surface* $\bar{S}$ *at the point* $\bar{P}$.

We now prove the following result. *The determinants* $|\bar{g}_{\alpha\beta}|$ *and* $|\bar{b}_{\alpha\beta}|$ *at the point* $\bar{P}$ *of the surface* $\bar{S}$ *are given by*

$$|\bar{g}_{\alpha\beta}| = (1 + \sigma^2 K - 2\,\sigma\Omega)^2\, |g_{\alpha\beta}|, \tag{24.12}$$

$$|\bar{b}_{\alpha\beta}| = (1 + \sigma^2 K - 2\,\sigma\Omega)\, |b_{\alpha\beta}|. \tag{24.13}$$

To prove this result we first set up the equations

$$|\bar{g}_{\alpha\beta}| = \tfrac{1}{2}\, e^{\alpha\mu}\, e^{\beta\nu}\, \bar{g}_{\alpha\beta}\, \bar{g}_{\mu\nu}; \qquad |\bar{b}_{\alpha\beta}| = \tfrac{1}{2}\, e^{\alpha\mu}\, e^{\beta\nu}\, \bar{b}_{\alpha\beta}\, \bar{b}_{\mu\gamma} \tag{24.14}$$

for the determinants in question. For convenience in carrying out the required operations let us now write the equations (24.8) and (24.11) as

$$\bar{g}_{\alpha\beta} = p g_{\alpha\beta} + q b_{\alpha\beta}, \tag{24.15}$$

$$\bar{b}_{\alpha\beta} = r\, b_{\alpha\beta} + s\, g_{\alpha\beta}, \tag{24.16}$$

where

$$\left.\begin{aligned} p &= 1 - \sigma^2 K; \qquad & q &= -2\,\sigma\,(1 - \sigma\Omega), \\ r &= 1 - 2\,\sigma\Omega; \qquad & s &= \sigma K. \end{aligned}\right\}$$

Then, substituting (24.15) and (24.16) into (24.14) we obtain

$$|\bar{g}_{\alpha\beta}| = p^2\, |g_{\alpha\beta}| + p\, q\, e^{\alpha\mu}\, e^{\beta\nu}\, g_{\alpha\beta}\, b_{\mu\nu} + q^2\, |b_{\alpha\beta}|, \tag{24.17}$$

$$|\bar{b}_{\alpha\beta}| = r^2\, |b_{\alpha\beta}| + r\, s\, e^{\alpha\mu}\, e^{\beta\nu}\, g_{\alpha\beta}\, b_{\mu\nu} + s^2\, |g_{\alpha\beta}|. \tag{24.18}$$

In order to simplify the right members of (24.17) and (24.18) let us observe that

$$e^{\alpha\mu}\, e^{\beta\nu}\, g_{\alpha\beta} = |g_{\gamma\delta}|\, g^{\mu\nu}, \tag{24.19}$$

which follow immediately from the equations (6.7) defining the contravariant components $g^{\mu\nu}$. Now, multiplying both members of (24.19) by $b_{\mu\nu}$ and summing on the repeated indices, we obtain

$$e^{\alpha\mu}\, e^{\beta\nu}\, g_{\alpha\beta}\, b_{\mu\nu} = |g_{\gamma\delta}|\, g^{\mu\nu}\, b_{\mu\nu} = 2\, |g_{\gamma\delta}|\, \Omega, \tag{24.20}$$

where Ω is the mean curvature of the surface S at the point P. Making the substitution (24.20) and also using the relation (21.12) we find that

$$|\bar{g}_{\alpha\beta}| = (p^2 + 2\, p\, q\, \Omega + q^2\, K)\, |g_{\alpha\beta}|, \tag{24.21}$$

$$|\bar{b}_{\alpha\beta}| = (r^2\, K + 2\, r\, s\, \Omega + s^2)\, |g_{\alpha\beta}|. \tag{24.22}$$

Finally substituting the above expressions for p,q,r and s into (24.21) and (24.22) and again making use of the relation (21.12) we are led to the equations (24.12) and (24.13).

If we divide corresponding members of the equations (24.12) and (24.13) and then take account of the relation (21.12) we obtain the following result. *The Gaussian curvature* $\bar{K}$ *at the point* $\bar{P}$ *of the surface* $\bar{S}$ *is given by the equation*

$$\bar{K} = \frac{K}{1 + \sigma^2 K - 2\, \sigma K}\,. \tag{24.23}$$

To deduce an expression for the quantities $\bar{g}^{\alpha\beta}$ we begin with the equations

$$\bar{g}^{\alpha\beta} = \bar{\varepsilon}^{\alpha\mu}\, \bar{\varepsilon}^{\beta\nu}\, \bar{g}_{\mu\nu}, \tag{24.24}$$

which are equivalent to the above relations (24.19). Replacing $\bar{\varepsilon}^{\alpha\mu}$ and $\bar{\varepsilon}^{\beta\nu}$ in (24.24) by the values

$$\bar{\varepsilon}^{\alpha\mu} = \frac{e^{\alpha\mu}}{\sqrt{|\bar{g}_{ij}|}}; \qquad \bar{\varepsilon}^{\beta\nu} = \frac{e^{\beta\nu}}{\sqrt{|\bar{g}_{ij}|}},$$

and then making the substitutions (24.8) and (24.12) we immediately obtain the following result. *The contravariant components* $\bar{g}^{\alpha\beta}$ *of the fundamental metric tensor of the surface* $\bar{S}$ *at the point* $\bar{P}$ *are given by*

$$\bar{g}^{\alpha\beta} = \frac{(1 - \sigma^2 K)\, g^{\alpha\beta} - 2\, \sigma\, (1 - \sigma\Omega)\, b_{\mu\nu}\, \varepsilon^{\alpha\mu}\, \varepsilon^{\beta\nu}}{(1 - 2\, \sigma\Omega + \sigma^2 K)^2}, \tag{24.25}$$

in which the quantities in the right members have their previous significance.

Finally we seek the corresponding determination of the mean curvature

$$\bar{\Omega} = \tfrac{1}{2}\, \bar{g}^{\alpha\beta}\, \bar{b}_{\alpha\beta} \tag{24.26}$$

of the surface $\bar{S}$. Substituting the expressions (24.11) and (24.25) for $\bar{b}_{\alpha\beta}$ and $\bar{g}^{\alpha\beta}$ respectively the right member of (24.26) becomes

$$\left.\begin{aligned} &\frac{(1-\sigma^2 K)(1-2\,\sigma\Omega)\,\Omega + (1-\sigma^2 K)\,\sigma K}{(1-2\,\sigma\Omega+\sigma^2 K)^2} \\ &-\frac{\sigma\,(1-\sigma\Omega)\,(1-2\,\sigma\Omega)\, b_{\alpha\beta}\, b_{\mu\nu}\, \varepsilon^{\alpha\mu}\, \varepsilon^{\beta\nu}}{(1-2\,\sigma\Omega+\sigma^2 K)^2} \\ &-\frac{\sigma^2\,(1-\sigma\Omega)\, K\, b_{\alpha\beta}\, g_{\mu\nu}\, \varepsilon^{\alpha\mu}\, \varepsilon^{\beta\nu}}{(1-2\,\sigma\Omega+\sigma^2 K)^2}\,. \end{aligned}\right\} \tag{24.27}$$

But one can show that

$$b_{\alpha\beta}\, b_{\mu\nu}\, \varepsilon^{\alpha\mu}\, \varepsilon^{\beta\nu} = 2\, K; \qquad b_{\alpha\beta}\, g_{\mu\nu}\, \varepsilon^{\alpha\mu}\, \varepsilon^{\beta\nu} = 2\, \Omega. \tag{24.28}$$

In fact the first equation (24.28) follows readily from (21.11) and the second is a slight modification of (24.20). Making the substitutions (24.28) in (24.27) and combining the terms in this expression we are led to the result that *the mean curvature $\bar{\Omega}$ of the surface $\bar{S}$ at the point $\bar{P}$ is given by the equation*

$$\bar{\Omega} = \frac{\Omega - \sigma K}{1 - 2\,\sigma\Omega + \sigma^2 K}\,,$$

in terms of the mean curvature Ω and the Gaussian curvature K at the point P of the surface S.

25. Developable Surfaces. Minimal Surfaces

In this section we shall comment briefly on two well known types of regular surfaces S in the Euclidean metric space E of three dimensions. One of these is the *developable surface* which is characterized geometrically by the condition that it can be rolled, without stretching or tearing, upon a plane. This implies that the developable surface is *intrinsically flat,* i.e. that its curvature tensor vanishes (see Remark 1 in Sect. 13). *It can be shown in fact that a surface S is a developable surface if, and only if, its Gaussian curvature K is equal to zero.*

Special developable surfaces are (α) the plane, (β) the cone and (γ) the cylinder which can be considered as a cone whose vertex is at infinity. More generally it can be shown that a developable surface is a *tangent developable,* i.e. the locus of the tangents of a regular curve C in the Euclidean metric space E; the curve C is called the *edge of regression* of the tangent developable.

Another type of surface to which we wish to call special attention is the *minimal surface* which may be defined as a surface whose mean curvature Ω is equal to zero at each point. *At an arbitrary point P of a minimal surface S, not a plane, the Gaussian curvature K must be negative.* In fact we must have $\kappa_1 + \kappa_2 = 0$ over a minimal surface S from the second equation (21.14) where κ_1 and κ_2 are the principal curvatures of S; hence neither κ_1 or κ_2 can be equal to zero since otherwise we would have $\kappa_1 = \kappa_2 = 0$ and it would follow that the coefficients $b_{\alpha\beta}$ of the second fundamental form vanish over S (see Remark in Sect. 21); but the vanishing of the coefficients $b_{\alpha\beta}$ means that S is a plane (see Remark in Sect. 18) contrary to hypothesis. Hence $K = -\kappa_1^2 < 0$ from the first equation (21.14).

Minimal surfaces arise in the existence theoretic problem of finding a connected surface of minimum area bounded by a given simple closed curve in the space E. This problem, known as the problem of Plateau, has attracted the attention of a number of distinguished mathematicians. It was finally solved by J. Douglas, *Solution of the problem of Plateau,* Trans. Am. Math. Soc. **33** (1931), pp. 263–321.

For a detailed treatment of the geometry of the above and other surfaces of special type the reader is referred to the standard texts on differential geometry.

General References

L. P. Eisenhart, *Riemannian Geometry,* Princeton University Press, Princeton, New Jersey, 1926.

T. Levi-Civita, *The Absolute Differential Calculus,* Blackie and Son, London and Glasgow, 1927.

O. Veblen, *Invariants of Quadratic Differential Forms,* Cambridge Tracts in Mathematics and Mathematical Physics, No. 24, Cambridge University Press, London and New York, 1927.

O. Veblen and J. H. C. Whitehead, *The Foundations of Differential Geometry,* Cambridge Tracts in Mathematics and Mathematical Physics, No. 29, Cambridge University Press, London and New York, 1932.

T. Y. Thomas, *The Differential Invariants of Generalized Spaces,* Cambridge University Press, London and New York, 1934.

E. P. Lane, *Metric Differential Geometry of Curves and Surfaces,* University of Chicago Press, Chicago, Illinois, 1940.

A. J. McConnell, *Applications of the Absolute Differential Calculus,* Blackie and Son, London and Glasgow, 1943.

Subject Index